AUTHOR INDEX

CAMBRIDGE MONOGRAPHS
ON MECHANICS AND APPLIED MATHEMATICS

GENERAL EDITORS

G. K. BATCHELOR, PH.D.
Lecturer in Mathematics in the University of Cambridge

H. BONDI, M.A.
Professor of Applied Mathematics at King's College,
University of London

THE THEORY OF
HYDRODYNAMIC STABILITY

THE THEORY OF
HYDRODYNAMIC
STABILITY

BY

C. C. LIN, Ph.D.

*Professor of Mathematics at the
Massachusetts Institute of Technology*

CAMBRIDGE
AT THE UNIVERSITY PRESS
1966

PUBLISHED BY

THE SYNDICS OF THE CAMBRIDGE UNIVERSITY PRESS

Bentley House, 200 Euston Road, London, N.W.1
American Branch, 32 East 57th Street, New York, N.Y. 10022

First printed 1955
Reprinted with corrections 1966

First printed in Great Britain at the University Press, Cambridge
Reprinted by offset-lithography at The Gresham Press
Unwin Brothers Limited, Old Woking, Surrey
(L 4322)

To

THEODORE VON KÁRMÁN

A Token of Respect and Gratitude

CONTENTS

5 Boundary Layer over a Flat Plate

6 Other Nearly Parallel Flows

7 Examples of Stability Problems of Interest in Astrophysics and Geophysics

8 Mathematical Theory for the Stability of Parallel Flows

PREFACE

The subject of hydrodynamic stability is well known for its controversial nature. Although there are still many points unsettled, a more permanent outline of the subject has emerged through recent advances. It is now possible to give a more reasonable evaluation of the significance and limitations of the results of such studies.

The present volume is limited mainly to the study of the stability of the motion of a homogeneous viscous fluid, with respect to infinitesimal disturbances, that is, the natural modes of small oscillations of such a mechanical system. Many other interesting problems, such as the stability of the interface between two different fluids, are therefore left out. Even in the case of a homogeneous viscous fluid, it would not be very useful merely to compile a list of all the cases that have been studied. Fortunately, two distinct prototypes of instability are presented by the two simplest types of flow: namely, the Couette flow, first attacked successfully by G. I. Taylor, and the plane Poiseuille flow, first attacked successfully by W. Heisenberg. Both cases have since been treated by a number of other workers. A reasonably detailed treatment of these two cases will therefore form the central part of the theoretical development. It will be demonstrated that many other cases possess similarity to them. The case of the boundary layer will also be given extensive treatment because of the remarkable success of the experiments of Schubauer and Skramstad, other recent developments, and its importance in technical applications.

The problem of transition to turbulence, which is in practice more important than that of the stability of laminar motion, will not be discussed in detail in the present treatment. It will only be explained to the extent needed to clarify the role of the theory of stability of laminar flow.

I should like to record my thanks to Professor Theodore von Kármán for his guidance during my first work on this subject, and to Professor J. L. Synge for initiating my interest in it through his semi-centennial address to the American Mathematical Society. I also wish to record my thanks to many of my friends and collaborators for keeping me continuously interested in this subject. Without this, the present volume would not have been written.

Dr W. Wasow read Chapter 8 of the manuscript; Dr H. L. Kuo read Chapter 7. Various other chapters were read by Professor L. Lees, Dr R. C. Di Prima and Dr D. W. Dunn. To these people, I wish to express my thanks for various suggestions. The final revision of the manuscript was largely made while I held a Guggenheim Fellowship at the Graduate School of Aeronautical Engineering at Cornell University. To Professor W. R. Sears, Director of the School, and to his colleagues, I am indebted for their interest in this work and various useful suggestions.

The author wishes especially to thank Dr G. K. Batchelor for initiating the preparation of this volume, and to thank the staff of the Cambridge University Press for the excellent work they did in proof-reading and printing and for their co-operation in making its early publication possible.

C. C. L.

October 1954

NOTE ON THE SECOND IMPRESSION

A number of misprints have been corrected in this reprint, largely based on a list of corrections provided by Professor C. S. Yih of the University of Michigan, to whom I wish to express my sincere gratitude.

C. C. LIN

November 1964

NOTE ON SYMBOLS

There is some difficulty in deciding on a consistent system of symbols for the treatment of hydrodynamic stability. It is desirable to discuss the same quantity in both dimensional and dimensionless forms. It is also necessary to discuss the same quantity in terms of the total amount, the basic part, the disturbance, and the amplitude function of a wavy disturbance. The following general conventions are adopted in this volume:

(i) In general, the discussion of the physical problem is presented in terms of quantities with dimensions, and the formulation of the mathematical problem is in dimensionless form. This permits the proper dimensionless parameters to be brought out clearly. In the case of a homogeneous incompressible fluid, as in Chapter 4, there is little difference between the two forms, and the above rule is sometimes relaxed to permit discussion of physical concepts in terms of dimensionless quantities.

(ii) Some basic symbols:

	Dimensional form	Dimensionless form
time	τ	t
space coordinates	$x_i: x_1, x_2, x_3$	x, y, z
velocity components	$u_i: u_1, u_2, u_3$	u, v, w
temperature	Θ	T
pressure	Π	p
density	ρ_*	ρ
viscosity coefficient	μ_*	μ

(Similarly for other properties of the fluid.)

(iii) Basic motion is denoted by a superimposed bar, and disturbance by a dash, thus:

$$u_i = \bar{u}_i + u_i', \quad u = \bar{u} + u', \quad \dots.$$

The amplitude functions for a wavy disturbance are denoted by $\hat{u}, \hat{v}, \hat{w}$, etc.

(iv) An asterisk at the *upper* right-hand corner denotes a complex conjugate. An asterisk at the *lower* right-hand corner is an indication that the quantity concerned is dimensional.

(v) Whenever there is a possibility of confusion, the symbol D is used to denote differentiation instead of a dash.

CHAPTER I

INTRODUCTION

1.1. The problem of hydrodynamic stability

The existence of two types of motions of a viscous fluid—laminar and turbulent—immediately raises the question: Which type of motion is the more likely to occur? It has now been generally recognized that turbulent motion is the more natural state of fluid motion, and laminar motion occurs only when the Reynolds number is so low that deviations from it are liable to be damped out. For certain types of flow, it has been found possible to keep the flow laminar for higher and higher Reynolds numbers by keeping the disturbance smaller and smaller. The question then may be asked, for a given flow: Is it stable relative to infinitesimally small disturbances? This is the problem of hydrodynamic stability.

Mathematically, the problem is as follows: Suppose the system of hydrodynamic equations has a time-independent solution

$$\bar{u}_i(x_k), \quad \overline{\Pi}(x_k), \quad \overline{\Theta}(x_k) \tag{1.1.1}$$

for the components of velocity, pressure and temperature. Consider an initial-value problem with these variables slightly different from those in this steady-state solution. If the solution approaches this steady-state solution (1.1.1) as time $\tau \to \infty$, the motion is stable. Otherwise, it is unstable. It should be noted that instability does not necessarily lead to turbulent motion; it could lead to another state of laminar motion.

To solve the problem of hydrodynamic stability, one must, therefore, follow the solution of a system of non-linear (quasi-linear) partial differential equations, and the task is in general very difficult. In the usual approaches to the problem, the mathematical formulation is cast in a different way. We *assume* that, for small disturbances, the equations may be *linearized*; that is, we shall neglect terms quadratic or higher in the disturbances and their derivatives. The resultant linear system of equations contains time τ only through derivatives with respect to τ, and hence solutions containing an exponential time factor $e^{\sigma_* \tau}$ may be expected. The boundary conditions for the disturbances are usually homogeneous and we have a characteristic-value problem, with σ_* as the parameter. If *all* the characteristic values of σ_* have negative real parts, the motion is stable with respect to infinitesimal disturbances. If some of the characteristic values σ_* have positive real parts, the motion is said to be unstable. The reason for this definition is as follows: Supposing that the flow is given a disturbance, finite or infinitesimal, we may conclude that it will, in general, not die out completely. For, if a disturbance is to die out, it must first become so small that the linearized equations would be expected to be applicable. The small disturbance would in general contain an unstable mode, which does not die out. On the other hand, there would be deviation from the exponential growth of this mode when its amplitude attains a moderate size.

The validity of the process of linearization, even though it is so often used in various physical problems, has sometimes been questioned in connexion with the problem of hydrodynamic stability. In the literature, one finds claims of proof of complete stability according to the non-linear theory in cases where the linear theory definitely indicated instability. However, careful examination of the arguments involved indicates that these claims are not justified.

1.2. Mathematical formulation of the stability problem in an incompressible fluid

The stability theory will now be formulated in some detail in the case of incompressible fluids in the absence of external forces. The basic equations satisfied by the velocity components u_i and the pressure Π are the equation of continuity

$$\frac{\partial u_k}{\partial x_k} = 0, \tag{1.2.1}$$

and the Navier–Stokes equations

$$\frac{\partial u_i}{\partial \tau} + u_j \frac{\partial u_i}{\partial x_j} = -\frac{1}{\rho_*} \frac{\partial \Pi}{\partial x_i} + \nu_* \Delta u_i, \tag{1.2.2}$$

where ρ_* is the density, $\nu_* = \mu_*/\rho_*$ is the kinematic viscosity coefficient, and Δ is the Laplacian operator. At solid boundaries with prescribed velocities S_i the condition

$$u_i = S_i \text{ on boundary} \qquad (1.2.3)$$

must be satisfied.

If the boundary velocities S_i are independent of time, we may have a steady motion

$$u_i = \bar{u}_i(x_k), \quad \Pi = \bar{\Pi}(x_k),$$

satisfying (1.2.1) and (1.2.2) in the form

$$\bar{u}_j \frac{\partial \bar{u}_i}{\partial x_j} = -\frac{1}{\rho_*} \frac{\partial \bar{\Pi}}{\partial x_i} + \nu_* \Delta \bar{u}_i, \quad \frac{\partial \bar{u}_k}{\partial x_k} = 0, \qquad (1.2.4)$$

together with the boundary condition

$$\bar{u}_i = S_i. \qquad (1.2.5)$$

To study small disturbances of the steady motion, we seek solutions of (1.2.1) and (1.2.2) in the form

$$u_i = \bar{u}_i + \epsilon u_i^{(1)} + \epsilon^2 u_i^{(2)} + \dots, \quad \Pi = \bar{\Pi} + \epsilon \Pi^{(1)} + \epsilon^2 \Pi^{(2)} + \dots, \qquad (1.2.6)$$

where ϵ is a constant parameter and $u_i^{(1)}, u_i^{(2)}, \dots$; $\Pi^{(1)}, \Pi^{(2)}, \dots$ are functions of position and time. We demand that (1.2.6) shall satisfy (1.2.1), (1.2.2) and (1.2.3) for all values of ϵ in a range $0 < \epsilon < \epsilon_1$. Formal substitution of (1.2.6) into (1.2.1), (1.2.2) and (1.2.3) gives a sequence of sets of four equations, each set corresponding to a definite power of ϵ. The set corresponding to ϵ^0 is (1.2.4), with the boundary condition (1.2.5). The set corresponding to ϵ^1 is

$$\frac{\partial u_i^{(1)}}{\partial \tau} + \bar{u}_j \frac{\partial u_i^{(1)}}{\partial x_j} + u_j^{(1)} \frac{\partial \bar{u}_i}{\partial x_j} = -\frac{1}{\rho_*} \frac{\partial \Pi^{(1)}}{\partial x_i} + \nu_* \Delta u_i^{(1)}, \quad \frac{\partial u_k^{(1)}}{\partial x_k} = 0,$$
$$(1.2.7)$$

with the boundary condition

$$u_i^{(1)} = 0 \qquad (1.2.8)$$

on the solid boundaries.

A complete treatment would require consideration not only of (1.2.7) but also of the equations corresponding to higher powers of ϵ, together with the establishment of convergence of (1.2.6) and justification of the term-by-term differentiation. It is customary, however, to confine attention to the first-order equations (1.2.7) in accordance with the discussion in § 1.1. At any rate, the discussion of these equations is a necessary preliminary to a more complete investigation.

It is clear that equations (1.2.7) admit solutions with an exponential time factor $e^{\sigma_* \tau}$. Also, in many cases, it will be necessary to make the assumption of a periodic spatial dependence to take care of the boundary conditions at infinity.

To facilitate the final mathematical formulation of the problem, all the equations should be put into the dimensionless form by means of suitably chosen reference quantities V_* and L_* for velocity and length respectively. Only then would the number of relevant parameters become apparent. In the incompressible case, the dimensionless form of the basic differential equations may be obtained directly from (1.2.2) by formally putting $\rho_* = 1$, $\nu_* = R^{-1}$, where R is the Reynolds number defined by

$$R = \rho_* V_* L_* / \mu_* = V_* L_* / \nu_*. \tag{1.2.9}$$

1.3. Examples

We shall now formulate the stability problem for a few familiar steady motions, which are exact solutions of the Navier–Stokes equations (1.2.1) and (1.2.2). The first example will be treated in some detail to bring out the general ideas involved. Two other cases will be treated in brief outline. It will be seen from these examples that the formulation of the characteristic-value problems involved is indeed very simple. Their solution, however, can involve rather difficult mathematical problems.

Example I. Flow between two parallel plates. Let fluid occupy the region between two infinite parallel plates, which are either stationary or moving parallel to each other with uniform speeds. Take a Cartesian coordinate system with the x_1-axis parallel to the direction of motion and the plates at $x_2 = \pm b$. Consider an observer moving with the lower plate, and denote by U_s the speed of the upper plate relative to it. We see that equation (1.2.4) and the boundary conditions are satisfied by

$$\begin{aligned}
\bar{u}_1 &= (\tfrac{1}{2} U_s)(1 + x_2/b) + U_c[1 - (x_2/b)^2], \\
\bar{u}_2 &= \bar{u}_3 = 0, \\
\bar{\Pi} &= -\frac{2\mu_* U_c}{b^2} x_1 + \text{const.},
\end{aligned} \tag{1.3.1}$$

where U_c is the velocity at the centre of the channel when the plates are stationary. Let us now introduce the characteristic quantities

$$V_* = \tfrac{1}{2}U_s + U_c, \quad L_* = b, \qquad (1.3.2)$$

and define the dimensionless variables as follows:

$$\left. \begin{aligned}
t &= \tau V_*/L_*, & x &= x_1/L_*, & \dots; \\
u &= u_1/V_*, & u &= \bar{u} + u', & \dots; \\
p &= \Pi/\rho_* V_*^2, & p &= \bar{p} + p', & \dots.
\end{aligned} \right\} \qquad (1.3.3)$$

Then the equations (1.2.7) for the small disturbances become

$$\left. \begin{aligned}
\frac{\partial u'}{\partial t} + \bar{u}\frac{\partial u'}{\partial x} + v'\frac{d\bar{u}}{dy} &= -\frac{\partial p'}{\partial x} + \frac{1}{R}\left(\frac{\partial^2 u'}{\partial x^2} + \frac{\partial^2 u'}{\partial y^2} + \frac{\partial^2 u'}{\partial z^2}\right), \\
\frac{\partial v'}{\partial t} + \bar{u}\frac{\partial v'}{\partial x} &= -\frac{\partial p'}{\partial y} + \frac{1}{R}\left(\frac{\partial^2 v'}{\partial x^2} + \frac{\partial^2 v'}{\partial y^2} + \frac{\partial^2 v'}{\partial z^2}\right), \\
\frac{\partial w'}{\partial t} + \bar{u}\frac{\partial w'}{\partial x} &= -\frac{\partial p'}{\partial z} + \frac{1}{R}\left(\frac{\partial^2 w'}{\partial x^2} + \frac{\partial^2 w'}{\partial y^2} + \frac{\partial^2 w'}{\partial z^2}\right), \\
\frac{\partial u'}{\partial x} + \frac{\partial v'}{\partial y} + \frac{\partial w'}{\partial z} &= 0.
\end{aligned} \right\} \qquad (1.3.4)$$

In these equations, $\bar{u}, \dots, \bar{p}$ represent the basic flow, and $u', \dots, p'$ represent the disturbance, both sets being in dimensionless form. Indeed,

$$\bar{u} = \left(1 + \frac{2U_c}{U_s}\right)^{-1}(1+y) + \left(1 + \frac{U_s}{2U_c}\right)^{-1}(1-y^2). \qquad (1.3.5)$$

The boundary conditions at the plates are

$$u' = v' = w' = 0 \quad \text{at} \quad y = \pm 1. \qquad (1.3.6)$$

What should be the conditions at infinity? The precise discussion of this point presents certain difficulties. Physically speaking, no experiment is performed with an apparatus of infinite dimensions. Mathematically, it is possible to circumvent the difficulty by limiting the discussion to disturbances which are *spatially periodic* in the directions in which the fluid extends to infinity. This is suggested by the nature of the equations (1.3.4). Since all three of the variables x, z, t are *cyclic*, the coefficients of (1.3.4) depending on y only, the system admits solutions which are exponential functions in x and z, as well as in t. If the solution is to be bounded for x, z becoming both $+\infty$ and $-\infty$, the corresponding exponents must be purely imaginary. Thus, each of the components of the disturbance is the real part of an expression of the form

$$q' = \hat{q}(y) \exp\{i(\alpha x + \beta z) - i\alpha ct\}, \quad -i\alpha c = \sigma_* L_* / V_*, \quad (1.3.7)$$

where α and β are real. We now put, in $(1.3.4)$,

$$\left.\begin{aligned}
u' &= \hat{u}(y) \exp\{i(\alpha x + \beta z) - i\alpha ct\}, \\
v' &= \hat{v}(y) \exp\{i(\alpha x + \beta z) - i\alpha ct\}, \\
w' &= \hat{w}(y) \exp\{i(\alpha x + \beta z) - i\alpha ct\}, \\
p' &= \hat{p}(y) \exp\{i(\alpha x + \beta z) - i\alpha ct\},
\end{aligned}\right\} \quad (1.3.8)$$

with the understanding that the real part of the solution represents the physical quantity. The dimensionless amplitude functions $\hat{u}(y)$, $\hat{v}(y)$, $\hat{w}(y)$ and $\hat{p}(y)$ then satisfy the equations

$$\left.\begin{aligned}
\{D^2 - (\alpha^2 + \beta^2) - i\alpha R(\bar{u} - c)\}\,\hat{u} &= R(D\bar{u})\,\hat{v} + i\alpha R\hat{p}, \\
\{D^2 - (\alpha^2 + \beta^2) - i\alpha R(\bar{u} - c)\}\,\hat{v} &= RD\hat{p}, \\
\{D^2 - (\alpha^2 + \beta^2) - i\alpha R(\bar{u} - c)\}\,\hat{w} &= i\beta R\hat{p}, \\
i(\alpha\hat{u} + \beta\hat{w}) + D\hat{v} &= 0.
\end{aligned}\right\} \quad (1.3.9)$$

The boundary conditions $(1.3.6)$ become

$$\hat{u} = \hat{v} = \hat{w} = 0 \quad \text{at} \quad y = \pm 1. \quad (1.3.10)$$

Although the sum of the orders of the equations $(1.3.9)$ is *seven*, it is possible to rewrite the system into a system of *six* differential equations of the first order. This is done by introducing the six variables

$$(z_1, z_2, \ldots, z_6) = (\hat{u}, \hat{v}, \hat{w}, D\hat{u}, R\hat{p}, D\hat{w}). \quad (1.3.11)$$

Then the solution is required of the system of equations

$$\left.\begin{aligned}
Dz_1 &= z_4, \\
Dz_2 &= -i\alpha z_1 - i\beta z_3, \\
Dz_3 &= z_6, \\
Dz_4 &= \{(\alpha^2 + \beta^2) + i\alpha R(\bar{u} - c)\}\,z_1 + (D\bar{u})\,Rz_2 + i\alpha z_5, \\
Dz_5 &= -\{(\alpha^2 + \beta^2) + i\alpha R(\bar{u} - c)\}\,z_2 - i\alpha z_4 - i\beta z_6, \\
Dz_6 &= \{(\alpha^2 + \beta^2) + i\alpha R(\bar{u} - c)\}\,z_3 + i\beta z_5.
\end{aligned}\right\} \quad (1.3.12)$$

satisfying the boundary conditions

$$z_1 = z_2 = z_3 = 0 \quad \text{at} \quad y = \pm 1. \qquad (1.3.13)$$

This is then seen to be a characteristic-value problem. The usual secular determinant would lead to a relation among the parameters occurring in (1.3.12) of the following form:†

$$\mathbf{F}(c, \alpha, \beta, R, U_c/U_s) = 0. \qquad (1.3.14)$$

For a given steady flow, R and U_c/U_s are known; then c depends on the real dimensionless wave-numbers α and β. If the imaginary part of c is positive, the solution increases exponentially with time (cf. (1.3.7)), and the motion is unstable *with respect to that particular mode*. If it is negative, this particular mode of disturbance will eventually be damped out. If c is real, there is a possible neutral oscillation.

Often the discussion is limited to two-dimensional disturbances. This may be obtained from the above as the special case with $\beta = 0$. The system (1.3.9) or (1.3.12) can then be conveniently reduced to a single differential equation for $\hat{v}(y)$:

$$(D^2 - \alpha^2)^2 \hat{v} = i\alpha R\{(\bar{u} - c)(D^2 - \alpha^2)\hat{v} - (D^2\bar{u})\hat{v}\}, \qquad (1.3.15)$$

and the boundary conditions (1.3.10) become

$$\hat{v} = D\hat{v} = 0 \quad \text{at} \quad y = \pm 1. \qquad (1.3.16)$$

Equation (1.3.15) is often referred to as the Orr–Sommerfeld equation.

The formulation of the problem of hydrodynamic stability is therefore relatively simple. However, as we shall see, its solution leads to rather serious difficulties. The chief source of this difficulty lies in the fact that instability can often be expected only for large values of the Reynolds number R.

Example II. Flow between rotating cylinders (Couette motion). We shall now consider the motion of an incompressible fluid between two concentric rotating cylinders. We adopt a cylindrical coordinate system with the z-axis along the common axis of the cylinders. With any choice of the scale V_* and L_* for velocity and

---

† The symbol $\mathbf{F}$ is loosely used for some function of the arguments indicated. It does not designate any particular function, and may therefore vary from one instance to the other.

length, the basic equations are, in dimensionless form, as follows:

$$\frac{1}{r}\frac{\partial}{\partial r}(ru)+\frac{1}{r}\frac{\partial v}{\partial \phi}+\frac{\partial w}{\partial z}=0,$$

$$\frac{\partial u}{\partial t}+u\frac{\partial u}{\partial r}+\frac{v}{r}\frac{\partial u}{\partial \phi}+w\frac{\partial u}{\partial z}-\frac{v^2}{r}=-\frac{\partial p}{\partial r}+\frac{1}{R}\left(\Delta u-\frac{u}{r^2}-\frac{2}{r^2}\frac{\partial v}{\partial \phi}\right),$$

$$\frac{\partial v}{\partial t}+u\frac{\partial v}{\partial r}+\frac{v}{r}\frac{\partial v}{\partial \phi}+w\frac{\partial v}{\partial z}+\frac{uv}{r}=-\frac{1}{r}\frac{\partial p}{\partial \phi}+\frac{1}{R}\left(\Delta v-\frac{v}{r^2}+\frac{2}{r^2}\frac{\partial u}{\partial \phi}\right),$$

$$\frac{\partial w}{\partial t}+u\frac{\partial w}{\partial r}+\frac{v}{r}\frac{\partial w}{\partial \phi}+w\frac{\partial w}{\partial z}=-\frac{\partial p}{\partial z}+\frac{1}{R}\Delta w,$$

$$(1.3.17)$$

where $R=V_*L_*/\nu_*$, (r,ϕ,z) denote the coordinates (dimensionless)

$$\Delta=\frac{\partial^2}{\partial r^2}+\frac{1}{r}\frac{\partial}{\partial r}+\frac{1}{r^2}\frac{\partial^2}{\partial \phi^2}+\frac{\partial^2}{\partial z^2}, \qquad (1.3.18)$$

and (u,v,w) are respectively the components of velocity in the directions of increasing (r,ϕ,z). In this system of coordinates, the steady flow is given by

$$\bar{u}=\bar{w}=0, \quad \bar{v}=Ar+B/r, \quad P=\int(\bar{v}^2/r)\,dr, \qquad (1.3.19)$$

where A and B are defined by $A=A_*L_*/V_*$, $B=B_*/V_*L_*$, and

$$A_*=\frac{\Omega_2 R_2^2-\Omega_1 R_1^2}{R_2^2-R_1^2}, \quad B_*=-\frac{(\Omega_2-\Omega_1)R_2^2 R_1^2}{R_2^2-R_1^2}. \qquad (1.3.20)$$

In the last two formulae, R_1 and R_2 denote the radii of the inner and outer cylinders respectively, and Ω_1 and Ω_2 are their respective angular speeds.

The first-order equations for the small disturbances are

$$\frac{1}{r}\frac{\partial}{\partial r}(ru')+\frac{1}{r}\frac{\partial v'}{\partial \phi}+\frac{\partial w'}{\partial z}=0,$$

$$\frac{\partial u'}{\partial t}+\frac{\bar{v}}{r}\frac{\partial u'}{\partial \phi}-\frac{2\bar{v}}{r}v'=-\frac{\partial p'}{\partial r}+\frac{1}{R}\left(\Delta u'-\frac{u'}{r^2}-\frac{2}{r^2}\frac{\partial v'}{\partial \phi}\right),$$

$$\frac{\partial v'}{\partial t}+\frac{\bar{v}}{r}\frac{\partial v'}{\partial \phi}+u'\frac{d\bar{v}}{dr}+\frac{u'\bar{v}}{r}=-\frac{1}{r}\frac{\partial p'}{\partial \phi}+\frac{1}{R}\left(\Delta v'-\frac{v'}{r^2}+\frac{2}{r^2}\frac{\partial u'}{\partial \phi}\right),$$

$$\frac{\partial w'}{\partial t}+\frac{\bar{v}}{r}\frac{\partial w'}{\partial \phi}=-\frac{\partial p'}{\partial z}+\frac{1}{R}\Delta w'.$$

$$(1.3.21)$$

The boundary conditions are

$$u' = v' = w' = 0 \quad \text{on} \quad \begin{cases} r = r_1 = R_1/L_*, \\ r = r_2 = R_2/L_*. \end{cases} \tag{1.3.22}$$

Equations (1.3.21) admit periodic solutions in ϕ and z:

$$q' = \hat{q}(r) \exp\{\sigma t + in\phi + i\lambda z\}, \quad \sigma = \sigma_* L_*/V_*, \tag{1.3.23}$$

where n and λ are real. In fact, n must be an integer. Analysis of the general case is still lacking; existing work deals with the special case of rotational symmetry: $n = 0$. The solution is independent of ϕ, but the component of velocity v' is not equal to zero.

With rotational symmetry, the motion may be represented in terms of a stream function ψ such that

$$u = -\frac{1}{r}\frac{\partial}{\partial z}(r\psi), \quad w = \frac{1}{r}\frac{\partial}{\partial r}(r\psi). \tag{1.3.24}$$

The disturbance may then be conveniently represented in the form

$$\psi' = -i\hat{\psi}(r)\exp(\sigma t + i\lambda z), \quad v' = \hat{v}(r)\exp(\sigma t + i\lambda z), \tag{1.3.25}$$

where the functions $\hat{\psi}$, $\hat{v}$ and the constant σ may be complex; the constant λ is real, and we may suppose it positive without loss of generality. The actual stream function and azimuthal velocity are to be found by taking the real parts of (1.3.25). With (1.3.25) and (1.3.24), the disturbance equations (1.3.21) reduce to the two ordinary differential equations

$$\left.\begin{array}{l} (L - \lambda^2 - \sigma R)(L - \lambda^2)\hat{\psi} = -2\lambda R\left(A + \dfrac{B}{r^2}\right)\hat{v}, \\[2mm] (L - \lambda^2 - \sigma R)\hat{v} = -2\lambda RA\hat{\psi}, \end{array}\right\} \tag{1.3.26}$$

where

$$L = \frac{d^2}{dr^2} + \frac{1}{r}\frac{d}{dr} - \frac{1}{r^2} = \frac{d}{dr}\left(\frac{d}{dr} + \frac{1}{r}\right). \tag{1.3.27}$$

The boundary conditions (1.3.22) become

$$\hat{\psi} = \frac{d\hat{\psi}}{dr} = \hat{v} = 0 \quad \text{for} \quad r = r_1, r_2. \tag{1.3.28}$$

The system of equations (1.3.26) and (1.3.28) will be consistent only if the constants σ, λ, A, B, R satisfy a characteristic equation of the form

$$F(\sigma, \lambda, R, A, B, r_1, r_2) = 0. \tag{1.3.29}$$

So far, the choice of the characteristic quantities V_* and L_* has been unspecified. If we now put

$$L_* = R_1, \quad V_* = \Omega_1 R_1, \tag{1.3.30}$$

(provided that $\Omega_1 \neq 0$) we have

$$
\left.
\begin{array}{l}
A = \{(R_2/R_1)^2 (\Omega_2/\Omega_1) - 1\}/\{(R_2/R_1)^2 - 1\}, \\
B = -(R_2/R_1)^2\{(\Omega_2/\Omega_1) - 1\}/\{(R_2/R_1)^2 - 1\}, \\
r_1 = 1, \quad r_2 = R_2/R_1,
\end{array}
\right\} \tag{1.3.31}
$$

and equation (1.3.29) reduces to

$$\mathbf{F}(\sigma, \lambda, R, R_2/R_1, \Omega_2/\Omega_1) = 0. \tag{1.3.32}$$

For a given steady flow, R, R_2/R_1, Ω_2/Ω_1 are assigned. Thus, the relation (1.3.32) determines the complex parameter σ for each wavenumber λ of the disturbance.

Example III. Flow through a circular pipe (Poiseuille motion). The steady flow through a circular pipe is represented by another simple solution of (1.3.17). In fact, if the radius of the pipe and the velocity at the centre are taken as the reference quantities, the solution is

$$\bar{u} = \bar{v} = 0, \quad \bar{w} = 1 - r^2, \quad \bar{p} = -4z/R + \text{const.} \tag{1.3.33}$$

The first-order equations of disturbance again admit solutions of type (1.3.23). Usual discussions are limited to disturbances with axial symmetry. In such a case, the use of a stream function again simplifies the analysis. If we introduce the disturbance stream function in the form (1.3.25) with $v' = 0$, we obtain for $\hat{\psi}$ the differential equation

$$\{(L - \lambda^2) - [\sigma + i\lambda R(1 - r^2)]\}\{L - \lambda^2\}\hat{\psi} = 0, \tag{1.3.34}$$

where L is again given by (1.3.27). The boundary conditions are

$$\hat{\psi} \text{ regular for } r = 0 \quad \text{and} \quad \hat{\psi} = \frac{\mathrm{d}\hat{\psi}}{\mathrm{d}r} = 0 \quad \text{for} \quad r = 1. \tag{1.3.35}$$

The secular equation is a relation of the form

$$\mathbf{F}(\sigma, \lambda, R) = 0. \tag{1.3.36}$$

For given R, it determines σ as a function of the wave-number λ.

If the flow has only rotational symmetry, the above discussions still apply to the components of velocities u' and w'. It can be readily shown (Synge, 1938b) that the equation governing v' has only stable solutions. Thus, as far as the stability problem is concerned, the case of rotational symmetry is not more general than that of axial symmetry.

1.4. Some general remarks

The previous examples serve to illustrate how easily problems of hydrodynamic stability can be formulated as definite characteristic-value problems. The simplicity of the final equation would even induce one to believe that such problems may not be difficult to solve. It is therefore natural to attempt to obtain simple general conclusions concerning the stability characteristics without detailed calculations. If such attempts are successful, it may be reasonably expected that the general conclusions thus obtained can be given a simple physical interpretation.

There has been some success in these attempts, notably in the following two directions: first, the establishment of necessary and sufficient conditions for instability when the effect of viscosity is neglected; secondly, the establishment of sufficient conditions for stability with the inclusion of the effect of viscosity. However, conditions of the first category are sometimes misleading, if not carefully interpreted, and those of the second category are often too weak. Most of the conclusive results depend, as yet, on a direct solution of the characteristic-value problem in each individual case, frequently involving elaborate numerical work and sometimes much controversy.

To appreciate the complexity of the situation, let us survey briefly our existing knowledge concerning the examples discussed above.

(i) *Plane Couette motion.* If $U_c = 0$ in Example I, the fluid motion is a simple shear caused by the relative motion of the two plates. This is obviously the simplest laminar motion conceivable, and one might also expect a simple stability problem. In fact, this is partially true. A fundamental system of four independent solutions can be readily found for the equation (1.3.15). However, no conclusive answer has yet been reached concerning this problem even today. All existing investigations tend to show that the flow is stable.†

---

† The most recent progress in this direction was made was Wasow (1953 a).

But to show that the motion is stable with respect to *all* modes of infinitesimal disturbances still remains to be done.

(ii) *Poiseuille motion*. In looking for a simple experiment, which might be correlated with theory, the flow through a circular pipe due to a pressure difference would naturally come to one's mind (Example III). In this case, the stability problem formulated above also has some simplicity in that two of the four independent solutions of (1.3.33) can be explicitly obtained. However, the present status of this problem is very similar to that of the previous one.†
Explanation of transition cannot be based only on the approach formulated above.‡

(iii) *Couette motion* (*Example II*). The flow between rotating cylinders is also easy to establish experimentally. In this case, one may expect the complication of the centrifugal force. Actually, this effect makes the stability problem more amenable to analysis, and we have, in the case of Couette motion, the first dramatic success of the theory of hydrodynamic stability in the important work of G. I. Taylor (1923). Taylor's analysis, though elaborate, is not controversial. He also checked his theory with experiments. Later workers, both theoretical and experimental, all agreed with his conclusions. It is recognized that the instability is associated with the centrifugal force, and that viscosity tends to damp out the disturbances. It is also recognized that as the speed is increased, a pattern of secondary flow is first established. Transition to turbulence occurs only at higher speeds.

(iv) *Plane Poiseuille motion*. If $U_s=0$ in Example I, we have a symmetric parabolic velocity distribution in a stationary channel. Although the experimental set-up of such a flow may be more difficult that the two previous cases, it would appear to be a simpler problem from the theoretical point of view. However, the theoretical developments turned out to be highly controversial. Although Heisenberg (1924) concluded that the flow is unstable, several later workers reached the conclusion that it is stable. There appear to be two reasons why it was difficult for Heisenberg's conclusion to be readily accepted. First, the asymptotic methods used in attacking (1.3.15) were not free from obscure points. In fact,

† See, for example, Pretsch (1941 c).
‡ Cf. § 6.3.

recent work indicated that the asymptotic behaviour of the solution of (1.3.15) is indeed very complex, but the method given by Heisenberg was found to be a valid approximation. The detailed calculations following his scheme (Lin, 1944) were checked by direct numerical integration (Thomas, 1953) of the equation (1.3.15).

A second reason (not unrelated to the first) is the fact that viscosity plays a rather complicated role in the physical mechanism. On the one hand it has a damping effect. On the other hand, it is actually the cause of instability. Thus the flow becomes unstable only beyond a certain critical Reynolds number, but the extent of the instability eventually decreases with further increase of the Reynolds number beyond certain limits. This dual role of viscosity is not always easy to realize at once. Indeed, if one conjectures that the effect of viscosity is solely to damp out the disturbance, then the misleading conclusion that plane Poiseuille motion is stable follows immediately from a general criterion of Rayleigh (1880, see § 4.3) obtained by neglecting the effect of viscosity.

The above brief survey perhaps helps to show why it may be necessary to present the theory first for specific simple steady flows. In fact, in more complicated cases, other controversial discussions may be found in the literature. Thus Taylor (1938) raised doubt whether the change of the thickness of the boundary layer would not render useless the calculations of Tollmien (1929) and Schlichting (1933 a, b, 1935 a) for the instability of the Blasius regime. These calculations were later verified by the experiments of Schubauer and Skramstad (1947), and also checked by calculations using the scheme suggested by Heisenberg (Lin, 1944).

We shall therefore first present detailed studies of Couette motion (Chapter 2) and plane Poiseuille motion (Chapter 3). Fortunately, these two cases may also be regarded as two distinct prototypes of instability, with which many other cases can be compared. In Chapter 4 we shall give some general discussions of hydrodynamic stability, including a treatment of certain general criteria and their physical interpretation. This will be used as a basis for the examination of other important special cases. Instability of the boundary layer and some other problems of interest to mechanical and aeronautical engineering will be treated in

Chapters 5 and 6. Some problems of meteorological and astrophysical interest will be treated in Chapter 7. In the selection of these examples, preference is given to the simplicity of a problem, and its role in the illustration of basic principles, rather than its importance in applications. From time to time, attempts will be made to correlate a problem under discussion with the two prototypes.

A treatment of the stability theory will not be complete without a discussion of the delicate mathematical points involved. This will be the subject of the final chapter of this volume.

CHAPTER 2

STABILITY OF COUETTE MOTION

2.1. Recapitulation of the stability problem

In this chapter we shall study, in some detail, the stability of the flow between rotating concentric infinite cylinders. This problem was first solved, both theoretically and experimentally by G. I. Taylor (1923). Taylor's analysis was quite elaborate, and later authors have tried to use simplified methods.

Since interest in problems of hydrodynamic stability is at least partly attributable to the mathematical problems raised and the mathematical methods used, some of these methods will be described in some detail in this chapter. Before doing so, we shall first recapitulate the boundary-value problem derived in § 1.3, and indicate some simplification in the case when the radii of the cylinders are not very different from each other. This is the case in most of the experiments performed so far. We shall then examine briefly the dependence of the critical Reynolds number on the parameters of the motion, and show that certain interesting conclusions can be reached, which may be checked with experiments, even without the complete solution of the problem.

The steady flow between two rotating cylinders may be characterized by the following three dimensionless parameters:

$$R_2/R_1 > 1, \quad \Omega_2/\Omega_1 \quad \text{and} \quad R = \Omega_1 R_1^2/\nu_*, \qquad (2.1.1)$$

where R_1, R_2 are respectively the radii of the inner and outer cylinders, Ω_1 and Ω_2 are their angular speeds, and R is the Reynolds number. The angular speed Ω of the fluid motion at a distance r from the axis is given by

$$\omega = \Omega/\Omega_1 = A + B/r^2, \qquad (2.1.2)$$

where
$$A = \{(R_2/R_1)^2 (\Omega_2/\Omega_1) - 1\}/\{(R_2/R_1)^2 - 1\}, \\ B = -(R_2/R_1)^2 \{(\Omega_2/\Omega_1) - 1\}/\{(R_2/R_1)^2 - 1\}, \quad (2.1.3)$$

and r is in the dimensionless form referred to the characteristic length R_1. A rotationally symmetrical disturbance, spatially periodic in the (dimensionless) distance z along the axis of the cylinders and exponential in time, may be represented by

$$u' = \hat{u}(r)\cos\lambda z\, e^{\sigma t}, \quad v' = \hat{v}(r)\cos\lambda z\, e^{\sigma t},$$
$$w' = \hat{w}(r)\sin\lambda z\, e^{\sigma t}, \quad \lambda\hat{w}(r) = -\frac{1}{r}\frac{d}{dr}(r\hat{u}). \tag{2.1.4}$$

The first-order equations for small disturbances then reduce to

$$(L-\lambda^2-\sigma R)(L-\lambda^2)\,\hat{u} = 2\lambda^2 R\omega\hat{v},$$
$$(L-\lambda^2-\sigma R)\,\hat{v} = 2RA\hat{u}, \tag{2.1.5}$$

where

$$L = \frac{d^2}{dr^2} + \frac{1}{r}\frac{d}{dr} - \frac{1}{r^2} = \frac{d}{dr}\left(\frac{d}{dr} + \frac{1}{r}\right). \tag{2.1.6}$$

Equation (2.1.5) is to be solved subject to the boundary conditions

$$\hat{u} = \frac{d\hat{u}}{dr} = \hat{v} = 0 \quad \text{for} \quad r = 1 \text{ and } r = R_2/R_1. \tag{2.1.7}$$

This leads to a characteristic-value problem with a secular equation of the form

$$F(\sigma, \lambda; R_2/R_1, \Omega_2/\Omega_1, R) = 0. \tag{2.1.8}$$

Apart from some changes in notation, the above formulation is substantially the same as that given in § 1.3. Before going into the details of the solution of the characteristic-value problem, let us examine some of its general features.

The system (2.1.5) is simplest when ω is a constant. Since $\omega = 1$ on the inner cylinder, and $\omega = \Omega_2/\Omega_1$ on the outer one, this may be expected for $\Omega_2/\Omega_1 = 1$. In fact, in this case, $A = 1$ and $B = 0$, and the fluid is indeed rotating uniformly. However, Synge (1938a) has conclusively shown that the motion is stable if $A > 0$, i.e. if

$$\Omega_2 R_2^2 > \Omega_1 R_1^2. \tag{2.1.9}$$

Thus, no instability may be expected from this simple case. Synge's proof depends on appropriate handling of the equations (2.1.5) so that the sign of the real part of σ can be determined through certain positive definite integrals. By similar methods, he was able to show (1938b) that the flow is stable if

$$R < \lambda^2 \frac{(R_2/R_1)^2 - 1}{(R_2/R_1)^2 \, |(\Omega_2/\Omega_1) - 1|}. \tag{2.1.10}$$

Let us now consider the general relation (2.1.8) for the characteristic values. Suppose that λ, R_2/R_1 and Ω_2/Ω_1 are fixed and R is increased. If instability occurs, it will appear when R has such a value that σ has a purely imaginary root. It is also possible that σ is always real and passes through zero. Although there is no conclusive proof, the latter is usually *assumed* to be the case ('principle of exchange of stabilities').[†] In fact, the 'neutral' mode would then be a secondary flow. Thus, the critical value of R, marking the incidence of instability, will be the smallest positive root R of [‡]

$$F(0, \lambda; R_2/R_1, \Omega_2/\Omega_1, R) = 0. \qquad (2.1.11)$$

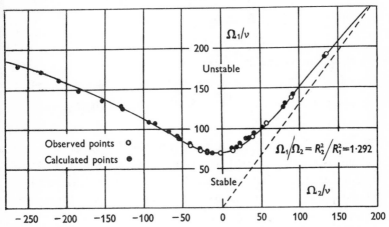

Fig. 2.1. Stability characteristics of Couette motion (after Taylor, 1923).

For a given basic flow, R_2/R_1 and Ω_2/Ω_1 are given, and hence R is a function $R(\lambda)$ of λ. The minimum value of $R(\lambda)$ will be the absolute critical value R_c, which depends on R_2/R_1 and Ω_2/Ω_1:

$$R_c = R_c(R_2/R_1, \Omega_2/\Omega_1). \qquad (2.1.12)$$

Thus, for a given steady flow, there is a definite critical Reynolds number. Associated with it, there is also a definite wave-number of the disturbance

$$\lambda = \lambda(R_2/R_1, \Omega_2/\Omega_1). \qquad (2.1.13)$$

Some of the experimental data obtained by Taylor are presented in fig. 2.1 together with his own theoretical results (see §2.4).

[†] Support of this assumption may be obtained from a consideration of the physical mechanism causing instability. See §4.2 and also §§7.3, 7.4.

[‡] Here the function F is the same as that in (2.1.8).

2.2. Approximate treatment of the problem

(i) *Case when the radii of the two cylinders are nearly equal.* Most of the experiments have been performed with the spacing between the two cylinders small compared with the mean radii. In such a case, the theoretical analysis can be simplified. In fact, it is clear that the relevant scale of motion of the disturbance would then be the spacing $R_2 - R_1$ between the cylinders, rather than the radius R_1. We should therefore introduce the following dimensionless variables:

$$\left. \begin{aligned} \xi &= (r-1)\{(R_2/R_1)-1\}^{-1} \quad (0 \leqslant \xi \leqslant 1), \\ \zeta &= z\{(R_2/R_1)-1\}^{-1}, \end{aligned} \right\} \tag{2.2.1}$$

which differ essentially from the previous ones by a factor $(R_2 - R_1)/R_1$. The corresponding dimensionless parameters are

$$k = \lambda\{(R_2/R_1)-1\}, \quad R' = \Omega_1(R_2-R_1)^2/\nu_* = R\{(R_2/R_1)-1\}^2. \tag{2.2.2}$$

The time scale is not changed, being still $1/\Omega_1$. The proper reference velocity is now $\Omega_1(R_2-R_1)$. The exponential factor associated with the disturbance is $\exp\{\sigma t + ik\zeta\}$. If we now make these substitutions in (2.1.5) and neglect higher powers of the small parameter $(R_2-R_1)/R_1$, equations (2.1.5) become

$$\left. \begin{aligned} (D^2-k^2-\sigma R')(D^2-k^2)\hat{u}_1 &= 2k^2 R' \omega \hat{v}_1, \\ (D^2-k^2-\sigma R')\hat{v}_1 &= 2R' A \hat{u}_1, \quad D = \frac{d}{d\xi}, \end{aligned} \right\} \tag{2.2.3}$$

where the disturbance-velocity components $\hat{u}_1$, $\hat{v}_1$ are also referred to $\Omega_1(R_2-R_1)$. The boundary conditions (2.1.7) become

$$\hat{u}_1 = \frac{d\hat{u}_1}{d\xi} = \hat{v}_1 = 0 \quad \text{for} \quad \xi = 0 \text{ and } \xi = 1. \tag{2.2.4}$$

The angular velocity ω is given by

$$\omega = A + B\{1 + (R_2/R_1 - 1)\xi\}^{-2}, \tag{2.2.5}$$

with A and B still defined by (2.1.3). Note that in this formulation the boundary conditions (2.2.4) are independent of any one of the parameters of the problem.

(ii) *Cylinders rotating in the same direction.* The critical condition (2.1.12) generally depends on the two parameters R_2/R_1 and Ω_2/Ω_1. When the cylinders are rotating with nearly equal speeds, suitable combination of parameters may be made so that this condition depends on fewer parameters. Indeed, one may approximate ω in (2.1.5) by some suitable average value $\bar{\omega}$ such as

$$\bar{\omega} = \frac{1}{2}\left(1 + \frac{\Omega_2}{\Omega_1}\right) \quad \text{or} \quad \bar{\omega} = \omega \quad \text{at} \quad r = \frac{1}{2}\left(1 + \frac{R_2}{R_1}\right). \quad (2.2.6)$$

Elimination of $\hat{u}$ from (2.1.5) then leads to

$$(L - \lambda^2)^3\,\hat{v} = 4\lambda^2 R^2 A\bar{\omega}\hat{v}, \quad (2.2.7)$$

after setting $\sigma = 0$ for the critical condition. Thus, we see that the characteristic value of the parameter $-4\lambda^2 R^2 A\bar{\omega}$ is a function of λ and R_2/R_1, the latter entering through the boundary condition (2.1.7). The minimum value of R, as λ is varied, corresponds to the minimum value of

$$K = -4R^2 A\bar{\omega} > 0. \quad (2.2.8)$$

Thus, for the critical condition,

$$K = K_c(R_2/R_1), \quad \lambda = \lambda_c(R_2/R_1). \quad (2.2.9)$$

If we use the approximation (2.2.3), the problem becomes even simpler. The equation analogous to (2.2.7) is

$$(D^2 - k^2)^3\,\hat{v}_1 = 4k^2(R_2/R_1 - 1)^4\,R^2 A\bar{\omega}\hat{v}_1, \quad (2.2.10)$$

and the boundary conditions (2.2.4) are independent of R_2/R_1. Hence the characteristic value of the Taylor parameter

$$T = -4\left(\frac{R_2}{R_1} - 1\right)^4 R^2 A\bar{\omega} > 0 \quad (2.2.11)$$

is a function of k alone. For the critical condition, both T_c and k_c are fixed. Thus, *the wavelength of the critical mode is a definite multiple of the (small) spacing between the two cylinders when they are close to each other and rotating in the same direction.* The critical Reynolds number is determined through a *definite value for* T.†

(iii) *Cylinders rotating in opposite directions.* If the cylinders are rotating in opposite directions ($\Omega_2/\Omega_1 < 0$), it is clear that the magnitude and sign of the average value $\bar{\omega}$ depend so much on the exact value of Ω_2/Ω_1 that $\bar{\omega}$ loses its significance. We need a better approximation. The next best than a constant is a linear function, and we may choose it to be the tangent to the (ω, ξ) curve at the point ξ_0,

† For the analogy between this case and a thermal problem, see § 2.3 and Chapter 7.

where ω is zero. We shall limit our discussion to the simpler equations (2.2.3). Now, if we write

$$\omega = s(\xi - \xi_0),\qquad(2.2.12)$$

where

$$\xi_0 = \left(\frac{R_2}{R_1} - 1\right)^{-1}\left\{\sqrt{\left(-\frac{A}{B}\right)} - 1\right\} = \frac{R_0 - R_1}{R_2 - R_1},\\
s = \left(\frac{d\omega}{d\xi}\right)_{\xi=\xi_0} = 2\left(\frac{R_2}{R_1} - 1\right)A\sqrt{\left(-\frac{A}{B}\right)} < 0,\qquad(2.2.13)$$

and R_0 denotes the (dimensional) distance of the point of zero speed from the common axis of the cylinders (fig. 2.2).

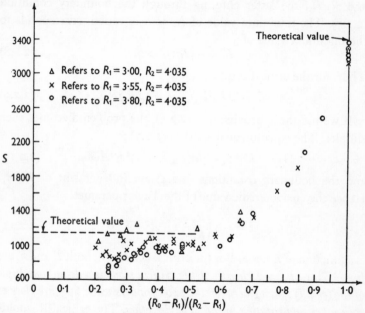

Fig. 2.2. Stability characteristics when cylinders
are rotating in opposite directions.

Eliminating $\hat{u}_1$ between the equations (2.2.3) and putting $\sigma = 0$, we have

$$(D_1^2 - k_1^2)^3 \hat{v}_1 = Sk_1^2(\xi_1 - 1)\hat{v}_1,\qquad(2.2.14)$$

where

$$\xi_1 = \xi/\xi_0,\quad D_1 = \frac{d}{d\xi_1},\quad k_1 = k\xi_0 = \lambda(R_0 - R_1),\\
S = 8R^2A^2\left(\frac{R_2}{R_1} - 1\right)^5 \xi_0^5 \sqrt{\left(-\frac{A}{B}\right)} > 0.\qquad(2.2.15)$$

The boundary conditions are

$$\hat{v}_1 = 0, \quad (D_1^2 - k_1^2)\,\hat{v}_1 = 0, \quad (D_1^2 - k_1^2)\,D_1\hat{v}_1 = 0, \atop \text{for} \quad \xi_1 = 0 \quad \text{and} \quad \xi_1 = 1/\xi_0.} \right\} \quad (2.2.16)$$

Thus, in general, the characteristic value, presented in the form S, depends on two parameters

$$k_1 = \lambda(R_0 - R_1) \quad \text{and} \quad \xi_0 = (R_0 - R_1)/(R_2 - R_1).$$

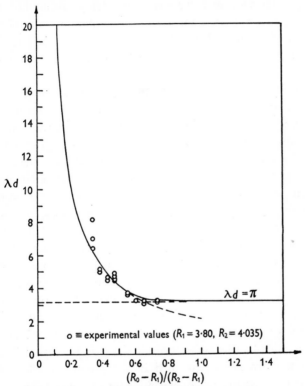

Fig. 2.3. Wavelength of the secondary motion.

The critical condition is obtained by minimizing S with respect to k_1, and is therefore marked by definite values of S and k_1 for each value of ξ_0. Figs. 2.2 and 2.3 show the plot of Taylor's experimental data according to this scheme. It is seen that there is a reasonably good correlation.

The parameters S and k_1 were first introduced by Meksyn through his asymptotic analysis. His work corresponds to the limiting case with $\xi_0 \to 0$. Thus, he obtained only fixed values of S and k_1. The above more general analysis is suggested by Lin and elaborated by Di Prima (1955), who also obtained the theoretical values shown in the figures.

2.3. Methods of analysis

There are many known methods for solving the characteristic-value problems formulated above. The original one used by Taylor in solving (2.1.5) is an expansion of the solution in terms of a complete set of orthogonal functions (see §2.4). The method is quite elaborate, but it still remains the only one ever used to handle the general case.

When the distance between the cylinders is small and the cylinders are rotating in the same direction, there is an analogy of the present problem to the problem of thermal convection due to temperature differences (see Chapter 7). This analogy was suggested by Low and Taylor, and demonstrated mathematically by Jeffreys (1928). Jeffreys found that the analogy is complete if, in the thermal problem, the fluid is contained between two infinite rigid conducting plates at top and bottom. In other cases, the equation (2.2.10) also arises, but the boundary conditions are different.

The solution of the characteristic-value problem (2.2.10), (2.2.4) has been treated in many ways. All of them give a value of approximately 1700 for the parameter T, as defined by (2.2.11). One method used by Jeffreys is to expand the sixth derivative of the solution function into a Fourier series, and obtain all the lower derivatives by integration. This avoids the difficulty of having to differentiate a Fourier series term by term. In fact, the differentiation process cannot be justified in the present problem, if the solution function itself were expanded into a Fourier series.

Pellew and Southwell (1940) obtained a variational principle for the Rayleigh–Jeffreys problem, and used it for obtaining the characteristic value. The calculation is very simple. Such a variational principle was obtained and used recently by Chandrasekhar for the more general case of an electrically conducting fluid in the presence of a magnetic field (see Chapter 7).

Neither Jeffreys nor Pellew and Southwell attacked the case of cylinders rotating in opposite directions. It would seem worth while to try to use some simple methods for the solution of (2.2.14) with the boundary conditions (2.2.16). Obviously, a variational principle may not be expected to hold, and the Galerkin method should be used instead. Such calculations were made by Di Prima (1955), with results shown in figs. 2.2 and 2.3. Since the term on the right-hand side of (2.2.14) changes sign between the boundaries, considerable care must be exercised in the choice of the approximating functions, if a successful approximation is desired with only a few terms. The reader is referred to Di Prima's original paper for the detailed discussions.

Meksyn (1946b) solved (2.1.5) by asymptotic methods, making use of the fact that λ is large. In his first approximation (and that is as far as he went), he is in effect treating (2.2.3) as an approximation to (2.1.5). This may be seen from an examination of his solution and the boundary conditions. Thus, the asymptotic solutions are really to be justified by the fact that k is large. It turns out that k is approximately π. This may appear to be small, but such values are often found to be large enough for asymptotic approximations.

Meksyn also used his asymptotic methods to discuss the more difficult case of cylinders rotating in opposite directions. Here, the formal solutions have branch points, which are close to each other, and Meksyn assumes that they may be regarded as coinciding. This is a rather bold step in the delicate problem of branches of asymptotic solutions. We shall not deal with his method here and refer the reader to his original papers.

2.4. Analysis of G. I. Taylor

We present below the analysis of Taylor following essentially the approach given by Synge (1938b).†

The appearance of the operator

$$L = \frac{d^2}{dr^2} + \frac{1}{r}\frac{d}{dr} - \frac{1}{r^2}$$

in (2.1.5) suggests at once the use of Bessel functions of order one: $J_1(\kappa r)$ and $Y_1(\kappa r)$, which are independent solutions of

$$(L + \kappa^2)\,\phi(r) = 0. \tag{2.4.1}$$

† Some of the symbols introduced in this section, such as ϕ_n, κ_n and Ψ_1, Ψ_2, etc., are not used in the same manner elsewhere in this monograph.

One can easily construct a system of orthonormal functions

$$\phi_n(r) = C_n\{J_1(\kappa_n) Y_1(\kappa_n r) - Y_1(\kappa_n) J_1(\kappa_n r)\}, \qquad (2.4.2)$$

satisfying the boundary conditions $\phi(1) = \phi(R_2/R_1) = 0$, where κ_n are the roots of

$$J_1(\kappa) Y_1(\kappa r_2) - Y_1(\kappa) J_1(\kappa r_2) = 0, \quad r_2 = R_2/R_1, \qquad (2.4.3)$$

and C_n is the normalizing factor, chosen so that

$$\int_1^{r_2} \phi_m \phi_n r \, dr = \delta_{mn}. \qquad (2.4.4)$$

We assume the existence of solutions of (2.1.5), (2.1.7), expansible in series of the above characteristic functions. However, we do not assume that these series can be differentiated term by term any number of times. Thus, even though we have

$$\hat{u} = \sum_{n=1}^{\infty} b_n \phi_n, \quad \hat{v} = \sum_{n=1}^{\infty} c_n \phi_n, \qquad (2.4.5)$$

we cannot substitute $\hat{u}$ in the left-hand side of the first equation of (2.1.5) to obtain

$$Q(\hat{u}) = (L - \lambda^2 - \sigma R)(L - \lambda^2)\,\hat{u}.$$

The expansion of $Q(\hat{u})$ in terms of ϕ_n must be obtained by calculating its coefficients directly:

$$Q(\hat{u}) = \sum_{n=1}^{\infty} q_n \phi_n, \quad q_n = \int_1^{r_2} Q(\hat{u}) \phi_n r \, dr.$$

To evaluate such integrals, we use the formula

$$\int_1^{r_2} r \phi_n L(F)\, dr = -\left[\frac{d\phi_n}{dr} r F\right]_1^{r_2} + \int_1^{r_2} r F L(\phi_n)\, dr. \qquad (2.4.6)$$

If we now multiply each of equations (2.1.5) by $r\phi_n\,dr$, and integrate to form 1 to r_2, and remember the boundary conditions (2.1.7), we obtain

$$-\left[\frac{d\phi_m}{dr} r \frac{d^2\hat{u}}{dr^2}\right]_1^{r_2} + (\kappa_m^2 + \lambda^2)(\kappa_m^2 + \lambda^2 + \sigma R)\, b_m = -d_m,$$

$$(\kappa_m^2 + \lambda^2 + \sigma R)\, c_m = -2RA b_m,$$

where

$$d_m = -2\lambda^2 R\left\{A c_m + B \int_1^{r_2} (\hat{v}\phi_n/r)\, dr\right\}.$$

If we now eliminate c_m, we arrive at an infinite system of linear equations in b_m, and the two quantities Ψ_1 and Ψ_2, which are the values of $r\, d^2\hat{u}/dr^2$ at $r = 1$ and $r = r_2$ respectively. This may be written as follows:

$$(\kappa_m^2 + \lambda^2)^{-1} \Phi_m^{(1)} \Psi_1 - (\kappa_m^2 + \lambda^2)^{-1} \Phi_m^{(2)} \Psi_2 + \sum_{n=1}^{\infty} (\delta_{mn} + E_{mn}) e_n = 0 \atop (m = 1, 2, \ldots),$$

$$(2.4.7)$$

where the following notation has been used:

$$e_m = (\kappa_m^2 + \lambda^2 + \sigma R) b_m,$$
$$E_{mn} = 4\lambda^2 R^2 A \left\{ A\delta_{mn} + B \int_1^{r_2} (\phi_m \phi_n / r) \, dr \right\} \{\kappa_m^2 + \lambda^2\} \{\kappa_m^2 + \lambda^2 + \sigma R\}^{-2},$$
$$\Phi_m^{(1)} = \left(\frac{d\phi_m}{dr}\right)_{r=1}, \quad \Phi_m^{(2)} = \left(\frac{d\phi_m}{dr}\right)_{r=r_2}.$$

$$(2.4.8)$$

Two more equations are supplied by the boundary conditions

$$\frac{d\hat{u}}{dr} = 0 \quad \text{at} \quad r = 1, r_2. \tag{2.4.9}$$

Term-by-term differentiation then gives

$$\sum_{n=1}^{\infty} (\kappa_n^2 + \lambda^2 + \sigma R)^{-1} \Phi_n^{(1)} e_n = 0, \quad \sum_{n=1}^{\infty} (\kappa_n^2 + \lambda^2 + \sigma R)^{-1} \Phi_n^{(2)} e_n = 0.$$

$$(2.4.10)$$

The infinite set of equations (2.4.7) and (2.4.10) linear in the quantities $\qquad \Psi_1, \quad \Psi_2, \quad e_1, \quad e_2, \quad \ldots, \qquad (2.4.11)$

then yields the characteristic equation in the form of the following infinite determinant:

$$\begin{vmatrix} 0 & 0 & (\kappa_1^2 + \lambda^2 + \sigma R)^{-1} \Phi_1^{(1)} & (\kappa_2^2 + \lambda^2 + \sigma R)^{-1} \Phi_2^{(1)} & \cdots \\ 0 & 0 & (\kappa_1^2 + \lambda^2 + \sigma R)^{-1} \Phi_1^{(2)} & (\kappa_2^2 + \lambda^2 + \sigma R)^{-1} \Phi_2^{(2)} & \cdots \\ (\kappa_1^2 + \lambda^2)^{-1} \Phi_1^{(1)} & (\kappa_1^2 + \lambda^2)^{-1} \Phi_1^{(2)} & 1 + E_{11} & E_{12} & \cdots \\ (\kappa_2^2 + \lambda^2)^{-1} \Phi_2^{(1)} & (\kappa_2^2 + \lambda^2)^{-1} \Phi_2^{(2)} & E_{21} & 1 + E_{22} & \cdots \\ \vdots & \vdots & \vdots & \vdots & \ddots \end{vmatrix} = 0.$$

$$(2.4.12)$$

It is clear that the numerical problem is formidable. When $r_2 - 1$ is small, the Bessel functions may be replaced by trigonometric functions and κ_n is approximately $n\pi/(r_2 - 1)$. Using this approximation, Taylor carried through the calculations for the case where the cylinders are rotating in the same direction, and obtained the following approximate formula for the critical Reynolds number R_c:

$$\left.\begin{aligned} R_c^2 &= \frac{\pi^4}{2}\left(\frac{R_2}{R_1}+1\right)\left(\frac{R_2}{R_1}-1\right)^{-3}\left(1-\frac{\Omega_2 R_2^2}{\Omega_1 R_1^2}\right)^{-1}\left(1+\frac{\Omega_2}{\Omega_1}\right)^{-1} \\ &\qquad\qquad\qquad\qquad < (0\cdot0571H+0\cdot00056H^{-1})^{-1}, \\ H &= \frac{1+\Omega_2/\Omega_1}{1-\Omega_2/\Omega_1}-0\cdot652\left(\frac{R_2}{R_1}-1\right). \end{aligned}\right\}$$

$$(2.4.13)$$

If, in the above formula, we neglect the terms $0\cdot00056H^{-1}$ and $0\cdot652(R_2/R_1-1)$, we obtain

$$R_c^2 = \frac{\pi^4}{0\cdot1142}\left(\frac{R_2}{R_1}+1\right)\left(\frac{R_2}{R_1}-1\right)^{-3}\left(1-\frac{\Omega_2 R_2^2}{\Omega_1 R_1^2}\right)^{-1}\left(1+\frac{\Omega_2}{\Omega_1}\right)^{-1},$$

$$(2.4.14)$$

or, in terms of the parameter T defined in (2.2.11), this is

$$T = 1709. \qquad\qquad (2.4.15)$$

CHAPTER 3

STABILITY OF PLANE POISEUILLE MOTION

3.1. Two-dimensional and three-dimensional disturbances

In §1.3, the basic equations are given for the study of the stability of a steady flow between parallel plates with respect to three-dimensional periodic disturbances. It is easily verified that the class of steady flows considered includes all exactly parallel steady flows. In fact, if we assume $u = \bar{u}(y)$, $v = w = 0$, we obtain a parabolic function for $\bar{u}(y)$ directly from the Navier–Stokes equations.

We shall now show, following Squire (1933), that the problem of three-dimensional disturbances is actually equivalent to a two-dimensional problem at a *lower* Reynolds number. In fact, if we introduce the following transformations

$$\begin{aligned}
\tilde{\alpha}\tilde{u} &= \alpha\hat{u} + \beta\hat{w}, \quad \tilde{v} = \hat{v}, \quad \tilde{p}\tilde{R} = \hat{p}R, \\
\tilde{\alpha}\tilde{R} &= \alpha R, \quad \tilde{c} = c, \quad \tilde{\alpha}^2 = \alpha^2 + \beta^2,
\end{aligned} \tag{3.1.1}$$

equations (1.3.9) may be written as

$$\begin{aligned}
\{D^2 - \tilde{\alpha}^2 - i\tilde{\alpha}\tilde{R}(\bar{u} - \tilde{c})\}\tilde{u} &= \tilde{R}(D\bar{u})\tilde{v} + i\tilde{\alpha}\tilde{R}\tilde{p}, \\
\{D^2 - \tilde{\alpha}^2 - i\tilde{\alpha}\tilde{R}(\bar{u} - \tilde{c})\}\tilde{v} &= \tilde{R}D\tilde{p}, \\
i\tilde{\alpha}\tilde{u} + D\tilde{v} &= 0.
\end{aligned} \tag{3.1.2}$$

This system of equations has the same structure as (1.3.9) with $\hat{w} = 0$, $\beta = 0$; i.e. (3.1.2) corresponds to a two-dimensional disturbance. The boundary conditions (1.3.10) obviously reduce to

$$\tilde{u} = \tilde{v} = 0. \tag{3.1.3}$$

Thus, each three-dimensional problem (1.3.9), (1.3.10), is equivalent to a two-dimensional problem (3.1.2), (3.1.3); which can be reduced to the form (1.3.15), (1.3.16). Hence it is sufficient to solve this two-dimensional problem and supplement it with the conversion (3.1.1). In fact, (3.1.1) shows that the equivalent two-dimensional problem is associated with a lower Reynolds number, since $\tilde{\alpha} > \alpha$. Thus, the minimum critical Reynolds number is given directly by the two-dimensional analysis.

Another method of arriving at the above results is physically more suggestive. The three-dimensional disturbance (1.3.8) is essentially a wave propagating in a direction oblique to the basic flow. If one takes a coordinate system with the new x-axis in this direction, it can be shown that only the component of basic flow *in this direction* affects the disturbance. Thus, the effective Reynolds number is reduced. This approach is particularly instructive in the compressible case, and a more detailed discussion of this idea will be presented there (Chapter 5).

3.2. Analysis of two-dimensional disturbances

We shall now re-derive the boundary-value problem (1.3.15), (1.3.16) in the following manner to stress the fact that (1.3.15) is essentially the equation for vorticity. A general two-dimensional motion can be specified by a stream function $\psi(x, y, t)$ such that

$$u = \frac{\partial \psi}{\partial y}, \quad v = -\frac{\partial \psi}{\partial x}. \tag{3.2.1}$$

In dimensionless form, the function $\psi(x, y, t)$ satisfies the vorticity equation

$$\frac{\partial}{\partial t}(\Delta \psi) + \frac{\partial(\Delta \psi, \psi)}{\partial(x, y)} = \frac{1}{R} \Delta \Delta \psi. \tag{3.2.2}$$

To study a small disturbance from a basic steady flow $\overline{\psi}(x, y)$, substitute

$$\psi(x, y, t) = \overline{\psi}(x, y) + \psi'(x, y, t) \tag{3.2.3}$$

into (3.2.2) and retain only the terms linear in the small disturbance $\psi'(x, y, t)$. For a parallel basic flow $\overline{u} = \overline{u}(y)$, $\overline{v} = \overline{w} = 0$, $\overline{\psi}(x, y)$ is a cubic in y, independent of x. The differential equation for ψ' is linear and has coefficients independent of x and t. Consequently, we may expect solutions of the form

$$\psi'(x, y, t) = \phi(y) e^{i\alpha(x - ct)}, \tag{3.2.4}$$

for which the linearized equation for ψ' becomes†

$$(D^2 - \alpha^2)^2 \phi = i\alpha R\{(\overline{u} - c)(D^2 - \alpha^2)\phi - (D^2 \overline{u})\phi\}. \tag{3.2.5}$$

The boundary conditions are $\psi'_x = \psi'_y = 0$, or

$$\phi = D\phi = 0 \quad \text{at} \quad y = \pm 1, \tag{3.2.6}$$

† For convenience of comparison with existing literature, $w(y)$ will sometimes be used in place of $\overline{u}(y)$ (Chapter 8). This will cause no confusion, since only two-dimensional motions are considered.

if the solid boundaries are at $y = \pm 1$. Thus, we have a characteristic-value problem resulting in a condition of the type

$$\mathbf{F}(\alpha, R, c) = 0. \tag{3.2.7}$$

For each pair of real values α and R there is a characteristic value c, in general complex. If the imaginary part c_i of c is positive, the disturbance is unstable according to the linearized theory. If $c_i < 0$, the disturbance is damped. If $c_i = 0$ there is a sustained oscillation. The condition $c_i = 0$ leads to a relation between α and R, or a curve in the (α, R) plane. This curve is usually referred to as the curve of neutral stability, or briefly, the neutral curve.

The stability of plane Poiseuille flow with respect to two-dimensional disturbances has been studied by many authors, often with contradictory conclusions. Heisenberg (1924) was the first to conclude the instability of the flow at sufficiently high Reynolds numbers, but he did not arrive at a critical value beyond which instability begins. Much controversy in the basic theory developed after Heisenberg's work, and discouraged workers from pursuing the work further along Heisenberg's line (see Heisenberg, 1950). After some clarification of the general theory, Lin (1944) made the detailed calculations of the neutral curve. Calculations of curves of constant c_i were made by Shen (1954) by a perturbation from Lin's neutral curve. These results are shown in fig. 3.1. The minimum critical Reynolds number is found to be 5300, based on the maximum velocity at the centre of the channel and its half-width.

The characteristic value problem (3.2.5), (3.2.6), can also be solved by direct numerical integration. However, because instability may be expected only for large values of the Reynolds number, the solution varies very rapidly in y, and very fine steps must be taken. The control of errors then becomes a difficult problem. These difficulties have, however, been overcome by L. H. Thomas (1953). His results, also shown in fig. 3.1, are in good agreement with those obtained by the analytical method.

The direct numerical calculations are quite lengthy, even with the help of a high-speed electronic calculator. For the limited amount of work performed, two weeks of machine time were required. Thomas estimated that this is equivalent to 100 years of work by hand computation. The choice of the values of the parameters in these calculations was helped by advance knowledge of the stability characteristics from the analytic methods, but the numerical values obtained are presumably somewhat more accurate.

Other workers have used analytical methods to study the stability of plane Poiseuille motion. Meksȳn (1946 a) used a method

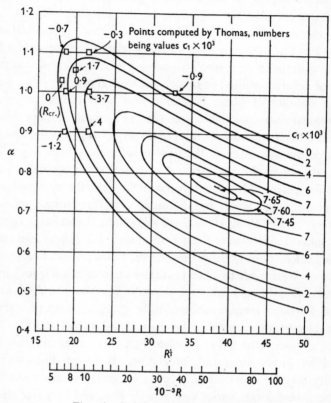

Fig. 3.1. Stability characteristics of plane
Poiseuille motion (after Shen, 1954).

similar to that used by Heisenberg and Lin, and obtained a minimum critical Reynolds number of 6800 after certain approximations. A different method was used by Pekeris (1948 b), who concluded that plane Poiseuille motion is stable at all Reynolds numbers. It is believed that this conclusion arises from the fact that Pekeris's series is essentially valid only for stable cases. The disagreement of his result with Lin's calculations led von Neumann to suggest the machine calculations made by Thomas. More recently, Tatsumi (1952 b) re-examined the work of Pekeris and Lin, and concluded in favour of the latter.

It would be highly desirable if the instability of this classical problem could be proved without resorting to such heavy calculations, as used in the methods mentioned above. This has been unsuccessful so far; only *sufficient* conditions for stability have been obtained by simple methods.

Many such conditions were obtained by various authors.† In the next section, we reproduce a class of such conditions obtained by Synge (1938 b) which are particularly elegant and useful.

3.3. Sufficient conditions for stability

It may be expected that only damped disturbances are possible for sufficiently small values of the Reynolds number R. It should be interesting, however, to establish more definite sufficient conditions of stability. A class of such conditions will be derived, following Synge (1938 b). The proof does not depend on the exact form of the velocity profile, which will therefore be unspecified.

If we multiply (3.2.5) by $\phi^* dy$ and integrate between $(-1, 1)$, we obtain

$$I_2^2 + 2\alpha^2 I_1^2 + \alpha^4 I_0^2 = -i\alpha RQ + i\alpha Rc(I_1^2 + \alpha^2 I_0^2), \qquad (3.3.1)$$

where

$$I_0^2 = \int_{-1}^{+1} |\phi|^2 \, dy, \quad I_1^2 = \int_{-1}^{+1} |\phi'|^2 \, dy, \quad I_2^2 = \int_{-1}^{+1} |\phi''|^2 \, dy,$$

$$Q = \int_{-1}^{+1} \{\bar{u} \, |\phi'|^2 + (\alpha^2 \bar{u} + \bar{u}'') \, |\phi|^2\} \, dy + \int_{-1}^{+1} \bar{u}' \phi' \phi^* \, dy.$$

If we now add to (3.3.1) its own complex conjugate, we obtain

$$2(I_2^2 + 2\alpha^2 I_1^2 + \alpha^4 I_0^2) = -i\alpha R(Q - Q^*) - 2\alpha Rc_i(I_1^2 + \alpha^2 I_0^2).$$
$$(3.3.2)$$

Now

$$|Q - Q^*| = \left| \int_{-1}^{+1} \bar{u}'(\phi' \phi^* - \phi^* \phi) \, dy \right|$$

$$\leqslant 2 \int_{-1}^{+1} |\bar{u}'| . |\phi'| . |\phi| \, dy.$$

If we denote the maximum of $|\bar{u}'|$ by q (equal to 2 in the present case), and apply Schwarz's inequality, we see that the last term is

† For a discussion of the earlier work, see, for example, von Kármán (1924).

bounded by $2qI_0I_1$. Thus, (3.3.2) reduces to

$$\alpha Rc_i(I_1^2 + \alpha^2 I_0^2) \leqslant \alpha RqI_0I_1 - (I_2^2 + 2\alpha^2 I_1^2 + \alpha^4 I_0^2). \qquad (3.3.3)$$

This relation gives an upper bound for c_i. If αR is small enough so that the upper bound is negative for all functions $\phi(y)$ satisfying the boundary conditions, the flow is stable. Thus, a *sufficient* condition for stability is

$$q\alpha R < \min\{(I_2^2 + 2\alpha^2 I_1^2 + \alpha^4 I_0^2)/I_0 I_1\}. \qquad (3.3.4)$$

Other more convenient forms of sufficient conditions can be derived as follows. If ξ and η are any two real constants, then

$$\int_{-1}^{+1} (\phi + \xi\phi' + \eta\phi'')(\phi^* + \xi\phi^{*\prime} + \eta\phi^{*\prime\prime})\,dy > 0,$$

from which we deduce

$$\eta^2 I_2^2 + (\xi_2 - 2\eta)I_1^2 + I_0^2 > 0,$$

and hence, from (3.3.3),

$$\eta^2\alpha Rc_i(I_1^2 + \alpha^2 I_0^2) < \eta^2 q(\alpha R)I_0I_1 - I_1^2(2\alpha^2\eta^2 - \xi^2 + 2\eta) \\ - I_0^2(\alpha^4\eta^2 - 1)$$

Stability is assured if the right-hand side is negative definite, which in turn follows from the inequalities

$$\left.\begin{array}{l} (\eta^2 q\alpha R)^2 < 4(2\alpha^2\eta^2 - \xi^2 + 2\eta)(\alpha^4\eta^2 - 1), \\ 2\alpha^2\eta^2 - \xi^2 + 2\eta > 0, \quad \alpha^4\eta^2 - 1 > 0. \end{array}\right\} \qquad (3.3.5)$$

Thus, for any pair of real values ξ, η satisfying the second set of conditions of (3.3.5) the first inequality gives a *sufficient* condition for stability. Three examples follow:

$$\text{(i)} \quad \xi = \eta = 1, \quad (qR)^2 < 4(2\alpha^2 + 1)(\alpha^4 - 1)/\alpha^2;$$
$$\text{(ii)} \quad \xi = \eta = 2, \quad (qR)^2 < 2(4\alpha^4 - 1);$$
$$\text{(iii)} \quad \xi = \eta = \tfrac{1}{2}, \quad (qR)^2 < 4(2\alpha^2 + 3)(\alpha^2 - 4)/\alpha^2.$$

These relations are useful in discussions of the general nature of the curve of neutral stability.

3.4. Method of asymptotic solutions: first method

So far it has not been possible to prove *instability* of plane Poiseuille flow at sufficiently large Reynolds numbers by means of methods similar to the above. It is necessary, at present, to attack the characteristic-value problem (3.2.5), (3.2.6) directly, by means of explicit solutions. Before doing so, let us first simplify the formulation of our problem somewhat by making use of the symmetry of our profile.

Since (3.2.5) is symmetrical in y, any solution $\phi(y)$ may be split up into an odd part $\phi_0(y)$ and an even part $\phi_e(y)$:

$$\phi(y) = \phi_0(y) + \phi_e(y).$$

Hence, if $\phi(\pm 1) = 0$, we have $\phi_0(\pm 1) = 0$ and $\phi_e(\pm 1) = 0$ separately. Similarly for the first derivative. Thus, both $\phi_0(y)$ and $\phi_e(y)$ must be characteristic functions (if not identically zero). Hence, it is sufficient to consider only odd and even functions in our characteristic-value problem. For even functions, the conditions

$$\phi'(0) = \phi'''(0) = 0 \tag{3.4.1}$$

must be satisfied. In fact, they are sufficient to guarantee the odd nature of ϕ, since $\phi(y)$ satisfies (3.2.5). Thus, our characteristic-value problem may be treated in the interval $(-1, 0)$, in which $\bar{u}(y)$ is monotonically increasing. For odd functions, the conditions (3.4.1) are replaced by

$$\phi(0) = \phi''(0) = 0. \tag{3.4.2}$$

Suppose now we have a fundamental system of four solutions of (3.2.5): $\{\phi_1,\ \phi_2,\ \phi_3,\ \phi_4\}.$

Then we may represent the general solution in the form

$$\phi = C_1\phi_1 + C_2\phi_2 + C_3\phi_3 + C_4\phi_4. \tag{3.4.3}$$

If we now impose the conditions (3.2.6) at $y = -1$, and (3.4.1) at $y = 0$, we obtain four homogeneous equations in the C's. The coefficient determinant must vanish. Thus

$$\mathbf{F}(\alpha, R, c) = \begin{vmatrix} \phi_{11} & \phi_{21} & \phi_{31} & \phi_{41} \\ \phi_{11}' & \phi_{21}' & \phi_{31}' & \phi_{41}' \\ \phi_{12}' & \phi_{22}' & \phi_{32}' & \phi_{42}' \\ \phi_{12}''' & \phi_{22}''' & \phi_{32}''' & \phi_{42}''' \end{vmatrix} = 0, \tag{3.4.4}$$

where (y_1, y_2) are used to denote the end-points $(-1, 0)$ and

$$\phi_{i\nu} = \phi_i(y_\nu), \quad \phi_{i\nu}' = \phi_i'(y_\nu), \quad \ldots \quad (i = 1, 2, 3, 4;\ \nu = 1, 2).$$

To evaluate the determinant, we need explicit representations of the solutions. Since the Reynolds number may be expected to be large, Heisenberg used asymptotic series for this purpose, considering only large values of αR. One natural way for obtaining such solutions is to write the solution as the formal expansion

$$\phi(y) = \phi^{(0)}(y) + \frac{1}{\alpha R}\phi^{(1)}(y) + \dots, \qquad (3.4.5)$$

so that the initial approximation $\phi^{(0)}(y)$ is a solution of the inviscid equation

$$(\bar{u} - c)(\phi'' - \alpha^2\phi) - \bar{u}''\phi = 0. \qquad (3.4.6)$$

Heisenberg obtained solutions as convergent† series of α^2 in the form

$$\phi(y) = (\bar{u} - c)\{q_0(y) + \alpha^2 q_1(y) + \dots + \alpha^{2n} q_n(y) + \dots\}, \qquad (3.4.7)$$

where

$$\left.\begin{aligned} q_{n+1}(y) &= \int (\bar{u}-c)^{-2}\,\mathrm{d}y \int (\bar{u}-c)^2 q_n(y)\,\mathrm{d}y, \\ q_0(y) &= 1 \quad \text{or} \quad \int (\bar{u}-c)^{-2}\,\mathrm{d}y. \end{aligned}\right\} \qquad (3.4.8)$$

In these formulae, the lower limit of integration is arbitrary, but will always be taken as y_1 below. These solutions will be denoted by $\phi_1(y, \alpha, c)$ and $\phi_2(y, \alpha, c)$ corresponding to $q_0(y) = 1$ and $q_0(y) = \int (\bar{u}-c)^{-2}\,\mathrm{d}y$ respectively.

Two other solutions are obtained in the form

$$\phi = \{\exp(\pm\sqrt{(\alpha R)}Q)\}\{f_0(y) + (\alpha R)^{-\frac{1}{2}}f_1(y) + \dots\}, \qquad (3.4.9)$$

where Q, f_0, f_1, ... can be obtained by formal substitution into (3.2.5) and comparing coefficients. We obtain

$$Q = \int_{y_c}^{y} \sqrt{\{i(\bar{u}-c)\}}\,\mathrm{d}y, \quad f_0(y) = (\bar{u}-c)^{-\frac{5}{4}}, \quad \dots \qquad (3.4.10)$$

In this formula, y_c is the point where $\bar{u} = c$, and is the branch point of the functions Q, $f_0(y)$, ... If c is real and less than unity, the point $y_c = -\sqrt{(1-c)}$ lies in the interval $(-1, 0)$.

Obviously, a proper branch of the function (3.4.9) must be chosen if y_c lies between the points y_1 and y_2 where the boundary conditions are to be satisfied.‡ This is one of the most difficult problems in the analysis. A detailed discussion of the mathematical issues involved will be given in Chapter 8. At the moment, let us be satisfied with the statement of the conclusion (which is to be obtained by heuristic

---

† For a discussion of the analytical nature of solutions of this type, see Lin (1945, Part I).

‡ See Langer (1940) for a determination of the domain in which the characteristic values of c must lie.

arguments in the next section) that one must take a path from y_1 to y_2 in the complex y-plane such that *the real part of Q increases monotonically*. In the present case (with $i = e^{\frac{1}{2}\pi i}$), this means that the path should be *below* the critical point y_c for nearly real values of c. Thus, for real c, we have

$$\left. \begin{aligned} \bar{u} - c &= |\bar{u} - c|, & \arg(Q) &= \tfrac{1}{4}\pi & \text{for} \quad y &> y_c, \\ \bar{u} - c &= |\bar{u} - c|\, e^{-i\pi}, & \arg(Q) &= -\tfrac{5}{4}\pi & \text{for} \quad y &< y_c. \end{aligned} \right\} \quad (3.4.11)$$

With the branch thus specified, we shall denote by ϕ_3 the solution represented asymptotically by (3.4.9) with the *negative* sign in the exponent. This solution *decreases* exponentially (and oscillates rapidly) as y increases along the real axis. In particular, we have

$$\left. \begin{aligned} \frac{\phi_{32}}{\phi_{31}} &= e^{-(\alpha R)^{\frac{1}{2}}} \left\{ \frac{f_0(y_2)}{f_0(y_1)} + \dots \right\}, \\ \frac{\phi_3'}{\phi_3} &= -\sqrt{\{i\alpha R(\bar{u} - c)\}} - \frac{5\bar{u}'}{4(\bar{u} - c)} + \dots, \end{aligned} \right\} \quad (3.4.12)$$

both very large in magnitude. In the above equation,

$$Y = \int_{y_1}^{y_2} \sqrt{\{i(\bar{u} - c)\}}\, dy, \quad (3.4.13)$$

and has a positive real part for $0 < c < 1$. The second relation in (3.4.12) is valid if $(\bar{u} - c)$ is not small. The other solution in (3.4.9) is denoted by ϕ_4. It also oscillates rapidly, but *increases* exponentially with increasing y.

With these properties of ϕ_3 and ϕ_4, it can be easily seen that the relation (3.4.4) can be approximated by

$$\begin{vmatrix} \phi_{11} & \phi_{12} \\ \phi_{21} & \phi_{22} \end{vmatrix} : \begin{vmatrix} \phi_{11}' & \phi_{12}' \\ \phi_{21}' & \phi_{22}' \end{vmatrix} = \frac{\phi_{31}}{\phi_{31}'}. \quad (3.4.14)$$

To show this, let us divide the third column of (3.4.4) by ϕ_{31} and the fourth column by ϕ_{42}'. If we make use of the first relation in (3.4.12) and an analogous one for ϕ_4, we obtain the approximation

$$\begin{vmatrix} \phi_{11} & \phi_{21} & 1 & 0 \\ \phi_{12} & \phi_{22} & 0 & 1 \\ \phi_{11}' & \phi_{21}' & \phi_{31}'/\phi_{31} & 0 \\ \phi_{12}''' & \phi_{22}''' & 0 & \phi_{42}'''/\phi_{42} \end{vmatrix} = 0.$$

Expansion of the determinant with respect to its last column gives

$$(\phi'''_{42}/\phi'_{42})\Delta_1 + \Delta_2 = 0,$$

where Δ_1 is the first principal minor, and Δ_2 is the cofactor of the second element in the last column. If we now apply the second relation in (3.4.12) and an analogous one for ϕ_4 and further assume that differentiation of the solutions $\phi_1(y)$ and $\phi_2(y)$ does not give rise to a corresponding increase of their order of magnitude, we see that a good approximation is given by $\Delta_1 = 0$, which can be easily reduced to (3.4.14).

The relation (3.4.14) may also be obtained in the following manner. If $\Phi(y)$ is a solution of (3.4.6) satisfying the condition $\Phi'(y_2) = 0$, then $\Phi(y) = \phi_1(y)\,\phi'_{22} - \phi_2(y)\,\phi'_{12}$. We now consider the solution

$$\phi = \Phi + c\phi_3,$$

which would still satisfy, to a good approximation, the conditions $\phi'(y_2) = \phi'''(y_2) = 0$, since $\phi_3(y)$ dies off rapidly as $y \to y_2$. If we now impose the conditions $\phi(y_1) = \phi'(y_1) = 0$, we obtain

$$\Phi(y_1)/\Phi'(y_1) = \phi_3(y_1)/\phi'_3(y_1), \tag{3.4.15}$$

which is identical with (3.4.14).

3.5. Reduction of the characteristic-value problem

If we now make use of the explicit solutions (3.4.7) to reduce the left-hand side of (3.4.14), we find, after some simple calculations,

$$-\frac{c\phi'_{22}}{\bar{u}'_1\phi'_{22} + \dfrac{1}{c}\phi'_{12}} = \frac{\phi_{31}}{\phi'_{31}},$$

which may be written in the form

$$\left.\begin{aligned}
\frac{\bar{u}'_1 c\phi'_{22}}{\phi'_{12}} &= -\left(1 + \frac{c}{\bar{u}'_1}\frac{\phi'_{31}}{\phi_{31}}\right)^{-1} \\
\text{or}\qquad 1 + \frac{\bar{u}'_1 c\phi'_{22}}{\phi'_{12}} &= \left(1 + \frac{\bar{u}'_1}{c}\frac{\phi_{31}}{\phi'_{31}}\right)^{-1}.
\end{aligned}\right\} \tag{3.5.1}$$

As we shall see later, these forms will be found to be particularly convenient for obtaining numerical results. In these expressions,

$$\left.\begin{aligned}
\phi'_{12} &= (1-c)^{-1}\{\alpha^2 H_1(c) + \alpha^4 H_3(c) + \ldots\}, \\
\phi'_{22} &= (1-c)^{-1}\{1 + \alpha^2 K_2(c) + \alpha^4 K_4(c) + \ldots\},
\end{aligned}\right\} \tag{3.5.2}$$

where
$$H_1(c) = \int_{y_1}^{y_2} (\bar{u}-c)^2 \, dy,$$

$$H_3(c) = \int_{y_1}^{y_2} (\bar{u}-c)^2 \, dy \int_{y_1}^{y} (\bar{u}-c)^{-2} \, dy \int_{y_1}^{y} (\bar{u}-c)^2 \, dy,$$

$$\dots\dots\dots\dots\dots\dots\dots\dots\dots\dots\dots, \tag{3.5.3}$$

$$K_2(c) = \int_{y_1}^{y_2} (\bar{u}-c)^2 \, dy \int_{y_1}^{y} (\bar{u}-c)^{-2} \, dy,$$

$$K_4(c) = \int_{y_1}^{y_2} (\bar{u}-c)^2 \, dy \int_{y_1}^{y} (\bar{u}-c)^{-2} \, dy \int_{y_1}^{y} (\bar{u}-c)^2 \, dy \int_{y_1}^{y} (\bar{u}-c)^{-2} \, dy,$$

$$\dots\dots\dots\dots\dots\dots\dots\dots\dots\dots\dots \tag{3.5.4}$$

With the formula (3.4.12) for ϕ_3'/ϕ_3, we have

$$\frac{c}{\bar{u}_1'} \frac{\phi_{31}'}{\phi_{31}} = \tfrac{5}{4} - Z^{\frac{3}{2}} e^{-\frac{1}{4}\pi i}, \quad \text{where} \quad Z = c\left(\frac{\alpha R}{\bar{u}_1'^2}\right)^{\frac{1}{3}}. \tag{3.5.5}$$

Thus we see that the right-hand side of (3.5.1) depends on the parameters α, R and c only through the particular combination Z. The left-hand side depends on the two parameters α and c. A further simplification results from the fact that, for real values of c, its imaginary part is given by†

$$v = -\pi \bar{u}_1' c (\bar{u}_c''/\bar{u}_c'^3)(1 + O(c^3)), \tag{3.5.6}$$

where $\bar{u}_c' = \bar{u}'(y_c)$, $\bar{u}_c'' = \bar{u}''(y_c)$. Thus, for moderately small values of c, v is a function of c alone (monotonically increasing in the present case). Thus, equation (3.5.1) may be written in the form

$$(u-1) + iv(c) = \mathscr{G}(Z), \quad \mathscr{G}(Z) = (Z^{\frac{3}{2}} e^{-\frac{1}{4}\pi i} - \tfrac{9}{4})^{-1}, \tag{3.5.7}$$

where $u + iv$ is defined by

$$u + iv \equiv 1 + \bar{u}_1' c \phi_{22}'/\phi_{12}', \tag{3.5.8}$$

and u depends on the two parameters α and c.

The structure of the equation now allows a very simple procedure for its numerical solution. Assign a value of c; the imaginary part of (3.5.7) determines Z, its real part in turn determines u. From u we determine α by (3.5.8); from Z we determine αR by (3.5.5), and hence R.

Detailed calculations following this procedure give a neutral curve in the form of a loop shown in fig. 3.1. Points inside the loop

† See Appendix to this chapter, p. 43.

correspond to unstable conditions. The general nature of this neutral curve is associated with the following behaviour of $\mathscr{G}_i(Z)$, the imaginary part of $\mathscr{G}(Z)$. It starts as zero when $Z=0$, reaches a maximum of $(2+\sqrt{2})/9$ when $Z^{\frac{3}{2}}=\frac{9}{4}$ and then decreases to zero as $Z^{\frac{3}{2}}\to\infty$. Thus, for $v<(2+\sqrt{2})/9$, there are two roots, which merge when $v=(2+\sqrt{2})/9$. This two-valued nature of the solution for given c is typical of this class of problems.

The following discussion may be used to anticipate the general nature of the neutral curve. For small values of $v(c)$, (3.5.7) gives

$$Z^{\frac{3}{2}}=\frac{81}{8\sqrt{2}}v \quad \text{and} \quad Z^{\frac{3}{2}}=\frac{1}{\sqrt{2v}}, \tag{3.5.9}$$

and the following corresponding values of u:

$$u=\tfrac{5}{9} \quad \text{and} \quad u=1. \tag{3.5.10}$$

From (3.5.5) we then have

$$\alpha R=\frac{(81)^2}{128}\bar{u}_1'\frac{v^2}{c^3} \quad \text{and} \quad \alpha R=\frac{\bar{u}_1'^2}{2c^3v^2}, \tag{3.5.11}$$

for the corresponding values of αR. Now, for small values of α^2 and c, it can be deduced† from (3.5.8) that

$$u=\frac{v}{\pi}\log c+O(1)+\frac{\bar{u}_1'c}{\alpha^2\displaystyle\int_{y_1}^{y_2}(\bar{u}-c)^2\,dy}(1+O(\alpha^2)). \tag{3.5.12}$$

Since u approaches constant values as $c\to0$ (equation (3.5.10)), this gives

$$\alpha^2=\frac{\bar{u}_1'c}{u}\left\{\int_{y_1}^{y_2}\bar{u}^2\,dy\right\}^{-1}. \tag{3.5.13}$$

Combining this with (3.5.11) and making use of the fact that $v\sim c$ in (3.5.6), we see that

$$R\sim\alpha^{-3} \quad \text{and} \quad R\sim\alpha^{-11}, \tag{3.5.14}$$

give the asymptotic behaviour of the two branches of the neutral curve for small α. One may then expect that these two branches join into each other, as v increases to $(2+\sqrt{2})/9$, and form a loop in the general form shown in fig. 3.1. Such tentative arguments can be made more convincing by using the sufficient conditions established in §3.3.

† See Appendix to this chapter, p. 43.

3.6. Method of asymptotic solutions: improved theory

Although the above analysis predicts correctly the general shape of the neutral curve, it is unsatisfactory in two important aspects. First, the correct branch of the asymptotic solution cannot be determined from the analysis developed so far. Secondly, the asymptotic branch $R \sim \alpha^{-3}$, although probably correct in general trend, is not reliable. This is due to the fact that the formula (3.4.9) for ϕ_3, or equivalently the formula (3.4.12) for ϕ_3'/ϕ_3, is not a good asymptotic representation when $Z^{\frac{3}{2}} \to 0$. Indeed, in such a case, the first term in the expression (3.4.12) for ϕ_{31}'/ϕ_{31} is much smaller than the second term. In fact, from (3.4.12) it can be seen that the two terms are of the same magnitude when $Z^{\frac{3}{2}} = \frac{5}{4}$. This suggests that one branch of the neutral curve, characterized by $Z^{\frac{3}{2}} > \frac{9}{4}$, is presumably reliable, while the other branch becomes increasingly inaccurate as $Z^{\frac{3}{2}}$ decreases with decreasing $v(c)$. We should therefore look for methods accurate for $Z = O(1)$. It will be seen that such an attempt also leads to an indication of the proper branch of the asymptotic solutions used above, and our problem may be regarded as satisfactorily solved in a heuristic manner. A full discussion of the mathematical issues involved will be given in Chapter 8.

For Z of the order of unity, we have

$$c = O(\alpha R)^{-\frac{1}{3}} \quad \text{or} \quad y - y_c = O(\alpha R)^{-\frac{1}{3}}.$$

Thus, we should seek a good representation of the solution $\phi_3(y)$ for small values of $y - y_c$. To do thus, we make a 'change of scale' by introducing

$$\eta = (y - y_c)/\epsilon \tag{3.6.1}$$

as the independent variable, where ϵ is a proper small parameter. The above discussion suggests that it should be $(\alpha R)^{-\frac{1}{3}}$. This choice can also be arrived at by considering the order of magnitude of the two terms ϕ^{iv} and $i\alpha R(\bar{u} - c)\phi''$ in (3.2.5) in the neighbourhood of y_c. We now write

$$\phi(y) = \chi^{(0)}(\eta) + \epsilon \chi^{(1)}(\eta) + \cdots, \tag{3.6.2}$$

and substitute it formally into (3.2.5). This method actually yields four solutions at once. They all contain the Hankel functions of order $\frac{1}{3}$:

$$H_{\frac{1}{3}}^{(1)(2)}\left[\left(\tfrac{2}{3}\right)(i\zeta)^{\frac{3}{2}}\right],$$

with $\zeta = (\bar{u}_c')^{\frac{1}{3}} \eta$. If one expands the Hankel functions asymptotically, for example

$$H_\nu^{(1)}(z) \sim \left(\frac{2}{\pi z}\right)^{\frac{1}{2}} \left\{\exp i\left(z - \frac{\nu\pi}{2} - \frac{\pi}{4}\right)\right\} \sum_{m=0}^{\infty} \frac{(-)^m (\nu, m)}{(2iz)^m}$$
$$(-\pi < \arg z < 2\pi), \quad (3.6.3)$$

the solutions can be identified† with those obtained in §3.4. In particular, the solution identifiable with ϕ_3 is

$$\tilde{\phi}_3 = \int_{+\infty}^{\zeta} d\zeta \int_{+\infty}^{\zeta} H^{(1)}[\tfrac{2}{3}(i\zeta)^{\frac{3}{2}}] \zeta^{\frac{1}{2}} d\zeta. \quad (3.6.4)$$

The restriction (3.6.3) on the argument of z corresponds to a path *below* the critical point y_c in the y-plane when $\bar{u}'(y_c)$ is nearly positive. This establishes the correct branch of the asymptotic solutions used in §3.4.

If we now use (3.6.4) for the evaluation of the quantity ϕ_{31}'/ϕ_{31} we obtain

$$\frac{\bar{u}_1'}{c} \frac{\phi_{31}}{\phi_{31}'} = -(1+\lambda) F(z), \quad (3.6.5)$$

where‡

$$\left. \begin{array}{l} F(z) = \dfrac{-\displaystyle\int_{+\infty}^{-z} d\zeta \int_{+\infty}^{\zeta} \zeta^{\frac{1}{2}} d\zeta H_{\frac{1}{3}}^{(1)}[\tfrac{2}{3}(i\zeta)^{\frac{3}{2}}]}{z \displaystyle\int_{+\infty}^{-z} \zeta^{\frac{1}{2}} d\zeta H_{\frac{1}{3}}^{(1)}[\tfrac{2}{3}(i\zeta)^{\frac{3}{2}}]}, \\[4mm] z = -\zeta_1 = (\alpha R \bar{u}_c')^{\frac{1}{3}} (y_c - y_1), \\[2mm] c = \bar{u}_1'(y_c - y_1)/(1+\lambda). \end{array} \right\} \quad (3.6.6)$$

Thus (3.5.1) becomes

$$u + iv = \{1 - (1+\lambda) F(z)\}^{-1}. \quad (3.6.7)$$

For small values of c, λ is small, and we have

$$u + iv = \mathscr{F}(z) = \{1 - F(z)\}^{-1}. \quad (3.6.8)$$

The function $\mathscr{F}(z)$ is shown in fig. 3.2 and table 1. Introducing $\mathscr{F}(z)$ back into (3.6.7) and solving for it, we obtain

$$\mathscr{F}(z) = \frac{(1+\lambda)(u+iv)}{1 + \lambda(u+iv)}, \quad (3.6.9)$$

where the right-hand side depends only on α and c. Its imaginary part varies only slightly with α.

† See Lin (1945).
‡ The function $F(z)$ was first used by Tietjens (1925).

To carry out the calculations, one may obtain a first approximation by using (3.6.8) in much the same way as (3.5.7) was used. Equation (3.6.7) can then be used for obtaining the final results by a suitable iteration procedure. Having obtained $\mathscr{F}_r$, $\mathscr{F}_i$, z and u, v for an assigned value of c, we must determine α and then

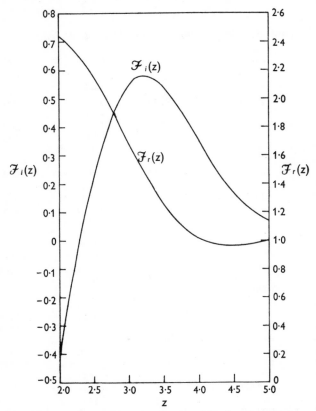

Fig. 3.2. Real and imaginary parts of the function $\mathscr{F}(z)$.

R from the values of u and z obtained by following procedures similar to those described in §3.5. The neutral curve shown in fig. 3.1 is then obtained. A perturbation from this neutral curve is then used for calculating lines of constant c_i.

The asymptotic branches of the neutral curves can be discussed in much the same manner as in §3.5. To compare the two treatments, let us first note, by comparing (3.6.8) with (3.5.7), that

$\mathscr{F}(z)$ corresponds to $1 + \mathscr{G}(Z)$. Furthermore, a comparison of the definitions of Z in (3.5.5) and of z in (3.6.6) shows that they are the same for small c. In fact, for large values of z,

$$\mathscr{F}(z) = 1 + \frac{i}{\sqrt{(2z^3)}} + \dots, \qquad (3.6.10)$$

Table 1. *The function $\mathscr{F}(z)$ and its first derivative*

z	$\mathscr{F}_r(z)$	$\mathscr{F}_i(z)$	$\mathscr{F}'_r(z)$	$\mathscr{F}'_i(z)$
1·0	0·80630	−2·60557	—	—
1·1			—	—
1·2	1·77012	−2·29854	3·71	2·781
1·3			2·54	—
1·4	2·26836	−1·71669	1·505	2·937
1·5			0·850	2·633
1·6	2·44985	−1·18600	0·4245	2·384
1·7			0·1390	2·127
1·8	2·48104	−0·75892	−0·06428	1·907
1·9			−0·2140	1·726
2·0	2·43927	−0·41253	−0·3337	1·573
2·1			−0·4377	1·443
2·2	2·35196	−0·12348	−0·5333	1·325
2·3			−0·6242	1·213
2·4	2·22724	+0·11916	−0·7108	1·1007
2·5			−0·7912	0·9833
2·6	2·06929	0·31558	−0·8625	0·8584
2·7			−0·9209	0·7254
2·8	1·88566	0·46043	−0·9627	0·5853
2·9			−0·9850	0·4414
3·0	1·68938	0·54872	−0·9853	0·2978
3·1			−0·9640	0·1590
3·2	1·49726	0·58082	−0·9223	0·0296
3·3			−0·8629	−0·0867
3·4	1·32516	0·56401	−0·7893	−0·1862
3·5			−0·7054	−0·2695
3·6	1·18429	0·51074	−0·6151	−0·3332
3·7			−0·5222	−0·3786
3·8	1·07982	0·43560	−0·4302	−0·4067
3·9			−0·3422	−0·4193
4·0	1·01118	0·35220	−0·2609	−0·4189
4·1			−0·1865	−0·4060
4·2	0·97361	0·27133	−0·1172	−0·3793
4·3			−0·0625	−0·3538
4·4	0·96056	0·20038	−0·01470	−0·3225
4·5			−0·0061	—
4·6	0·95989	0·13601	−0·0034	—
4·7			+0·0476	—
4·8	0·97659	0·09503	+0·1794	—
4·9			—	—
5·0	0·99582	0·07266	—	—

so that it is equal to $1 + \mathcal{G}(Z)$ to a first approximation. Thus, the new formulation (3.6.8) reduces to the old one for c small and z large.

There is also a general similarity to $\mathcal{G}_i(Z)$ in the behaviour of the imaginary part of $\mathcal{F}(z)$. As z decreases from large values, $\mathcal{F}_i(z)$ increases to a maximum of $0 \cdot 58$ at $z = 3 \cdot 21$ (as compared with $0 \cdot 54$ for $\mathcal{G}_i(Z)$ at $Z = 1 \cdot 73$), and decreases to zero at $z = 2 \cdot 294$ with $\mathcal{F}_r(z) = 2 \cdot 292$ (as compared with $Z = 0$, for $\mathcal{G}_i(Z)$, with $\mathcal{G}_r(Z) = \frac{5}{9}$). Thus, the two-branch nature of the neutral curve is again assured. The above discussions also indicate that one of the branches (corresponding to $z \rightarrow \infty$) must be the same as obtained before. The other branch, corresponding to $c \rightarrow 0$, $z \rightarrow 2 \cdot 294$, however, must be different, since the first set of equations of (3.5.9), (3.5.10), (3.5.11), are to be replaced by

$$\left.\begin{aligned} z &= 2 \cdot 294, \\ u &= 2 \cdot 292, \\ \alpha R &= (2 \cdot 294)^3 \, \bar{u}_1'^2 / c^3. \end{aligned}\right\} \qquad (3.6.11)$$

If we now make use of the same approximation relation (3.5.13), we have, in contrast to the first equation of (3.5.14), the relations

$$R = \alpha^{-7} \bar{u}_1'^5 \left(z \Big/ \mathcal{F}_r \int_{y_1}^{y_2} \bar{u}^2 \, \mathrm{d}y \right)^3, \quad c = \alpha^2 (\mathcal{F}_r / \bar{u}_1') \int_{y_1}^{y_2} \bar{u}^2 \, \mathrm{d}y. \quad (3.6.12)$$

In these equations, the numerical values of z and $\mathcal{F}_r$ are, respectively, $2 \cdot 294$ and $2 \cdot 292$. The other branch is given by

$$R = \alpha^{-11} (\bar{u}_1')^{11} \left(2\pi \bar{u}_c''^2 \int_{y_1}^{y_2} \bar{u} \, \mathrm{d}y \right)^{-1}, \quad c = (\alpha^2 / \bar{u}_1') \int_{y_1}^{y_2} \bar{u}^2 \, \mathrm{d}y, \quad (3.6.13)$$

in agreement with the second equation of (3.5.14).

APPENDIX TO CHAPTER 3

One of the main steps in the numerical calculation of the stability problem, as formulated above, is the evaluation of the expressions in the left-hand side of (3.5.1). This in turn depends on the evaluation of the integrals in (3.5.3) and (3.5.4). For these purposes, the following transformations bring out the general nature of the dependence on α and c of the functions involved, especially when these parameters are small. Because of its wide use, we shall outline the essential steps for the present case.

First, it should be remarked that all the integrals may be taken along the real axis with an indented path at the critical point y_c. The path should be taken below the real axis in that neighbourhood.

The type of transformation we introduce may be exemplified by means of the following. In equation (3.5.4) we introduce the relation

$$\int_{y_1}^{y} (\bar{u}-c)^{-2}\,dy = \int_{y_1}^{y_2} dy\,(\bar{u}-c)^{-2} \doteq \int_{y}^{y_2} (\bar{u}-c)^{-2}\,dy. \qquad (3\,\mathrm{A}.\,1)$$

Then
$$K_2(c) = K_1(c)\,H_1(c) - N_2(c), \qquad (3\,\mathrm{A}.\,2)$$

where $H_1(c)$ is defined in (3.5.3), and $K_1(c)$, $N_2(c)$ are defined as follows:

$$\left.\begin{aligned}
K_1(c) &= \int_{y_1}^{y_2} (\bar{u}-c)^{-2}\,dy, \\
N_2(c) &= \int_{y_1}^{y_2} (\bar{u}-c)^2\,dy \int_{y}^{y_2} (\bar{u}-c)^{-2}\,dy.
\end{aligned}\right\} \qquad (3\,\mathrm{A}.\,3)$$

The advantage of this transformation is that the inner integral in $N_2(c)$ is real except for the interval $y_1 < y < y_2$, which is small when c is small. Furthermore, the factor $(\bar{u}-c)^2$ is small in this interval and tends to make this part unimportant to the contribution to $N_2(c)$. The principal contribution to the imaginary part of $K_2(c)$ is then given by $K_1(c)\,H_1(c)$.

If we apply this idea to all the integrals involved in (3.5.2), we may obtain

$$\left.\begin{aligned}
\phi_{12}' &= (\mathrm{1}-c)^{-1}(\mathrm{1}-\alpha^2 H_2)^{-1}\left(\alpha^2 H_1 - \sum_{n=1}^{\infty} \alpha^{2n} M_{2n-1}\right), \\
\phi_{22}' &= K_1\phi_{12}' + (\mathrm{1}-c)^{-1}\left(\mathrm{1} - \sum_{n=1}^{\infty} \alpha^{2n} N_{2n}\right),
\end{aligned}\right\} \qquad (3\,\mathrm{A}.\,4)$$

where the functions $M_n(c)$ and $N_n(c)$ are defined by

$$\left.\begin{aligned}
M_n &= H_2 H_{n-2} - H_n \quad (n \geqslant 3), \\
N_n &= K_1 H_{n-1} - K_n \quad (n \geqslant 2);
\end{aligned}\right\} \qquad (3\,\mathrm{A}.\,5)$$

and the H's and K's are defined by relations similar to (3.5.3); for example,

$$\left.\begin{aligned}
H_2 &= \int_{y_1}^{y_2} (\bar{u}-c)^{-2}\,dy \int_{y_1}^{y} (\bar{u}-c)^2\,dy, \\
K_3 &= \int_{y_1}^{y_2} (\bar{u}-c)^{-2}\,dy \int_{y_1}^{y} (\bar{u}-c)^2\,dy \int_{y_1}^{y} (\bar{u}-c)^{-2}\,dy.
\end{aligned}\right\} \qquad (3\,\mathrm{A}.\,6)$$

If we now introduce (3 A. 4) into (3.5.8), we obtain

$$u + iv = \bar{u}_1' c \left(K_1 + \frac{1}{\bar{u}_1' c} \right) + \frac{\bar{u}_1' c}{\alpha^2} (1 - \alpha^2 H_2)(1 - \alpha^2 H_2 - \alpha^4 N_4 - \ldots)$$
$$\times (H_1 - \alpha^2 M_3 - \alpha^4 M_5 - \ldots)^{-1}, \quad (3 \text{ A. } 7)$$

where the imaginary part $v(\alpha, c)$ is mainly contained in the first term. Indeed, for small values of c, it is easy to show, by power series expansions of $\bar{u} - c$ around the point y_c, that

$$K_1(c) = \frac{1}{\bar{u}_1' c} + \frac{\bar{u}_c''}{\bar{u}_c'^3}(\log c - i\pi) + O(1). \quad (3 \text{ A. } 8)$$

We have then the basis for the relations (3.5.6) and (3.5.12).

CHAPTER 4

GENERAL THEORY OF HYDRODYNAMIC STABILITY

4.1. Physical mechanism of instability

In the previous chapters, the linearized theory of instability has been formulated in general and carried out in detail for two classical cases of steady flow. Certain mathematical problems are raised, which will be treated in detail in Chapter 8. Two important aspects in the general theory still remain not discussed, namely, (i) the behaviour of disturbances of finite amplitudes, and (ii) the general understanding of the physical mechanism. A discussion of the former problem is closely connected with the transition from laminar flow to turbulent flow, and a complete treatment is beyond the scope of this short monograph. Some discussions will be given in § 4.6 and again in § 6.1 in connexion with the boundary layer. The other sections in this chapter will be devoted to the clarification of the physical mechanism.

Certain basic mechanisms of instability can be easily visualized. For example, when heavier fluid lies on top of lighter fluid, gravitational forces will tend to cause instability. Related to this is the instability at the interface between a liquid and a gas, when there is an acceleration in the direction going from the liquid to the gas (Taylor, 1950). However, in the case treated in Chapter 3, the mechanism of instability is not so obvious.

It might be conjectured, from general physical arguments, that viscous forces will contribute to a stabilizing effect by tending to damp out the disturbances. If one further observes that instability generally occurs at large Reynolds numbers, one might reason that the principal features of the mechanism of instability may be obtained by first neglecting viscous forces, and incorporating it later as a stabilizing influence. There is also an obvious advantage of such an approach from the point of view of simplicity of analysis. Since the viscous terms contain spatial derivatives of the highest order, their neglect would reduce the order of the stability equations.

Lord Rayleigh had much success with the non-viscous analysis. From physical reasoning, he reached the following conclusion: If the effect of viscosity is neglected, the motion of rotating fluids is stable or unstable, depending on whether the square of the circulation increases monotonically outwards (for details, see §4.2). A comparison of this conclusion with fig. 2.1 shows that, when viscosity is considered, the actual motion is even more stable than indicated by this criterion. This agrees with the general understanding that viscous forces tend to damp out small disturbances.

Rayleigh also found that, for parallel flows to be unstable, the velocity distribution must show a point of inflexion. Later, Tollmien (1935 b) showed that this condition is also sufficient for velocity distributions of certain general types. A physical mechanism for interpreting this result was described by Lin (1945), using an acceleration formula derived on the basis of von Kármán's mechanism of vorticity redistribution† (1934). More recently, Rossby (1949) applied these ideas to the motion of polar air masses, fundamental in atmospheric processes.

In this case, however, a comparison of the conclusions in the viscous and non-viscous studies reveals the rather surprising result that *viscous forces can serve as a cause of instability*. In the case of plane Poiseuille flow, Rayleigh's criterion would certainly indicate stability in the absence of viscosity. This is, in fact, in agreement with the results obtained from detailed calculations. The motion is stable with respect to disturbances of a given wavelength, provided the Reynolds number is high enough (fig. 3.1). However, for wavelengths beyond a certain lower limit, there is always a finite range of Reynolds number for which the motion is unstable. Thus, an *increase* of viscosity could actually induce *instability*. On the other hand, the motion is completely stable if the Reynolds number is sufficiently low, as one would expect from the damping influence of viscous forces. The physical mechanism for this dual effect was described by Prandtl (1922) in connexion with the instability of the boundary layer. The viscous forces are shown to be capable of inducing a Reynolds stress, absent in the inviscid case. If this stress converts energy from the basic flow into the disturbance, it could

† Von Kármán first advanced these ideas in his discussion of the vorticity transfer theory in fully developed turbulence.

induce instability. Prandtl (1922, 1935) did not give a complete analysis of the direction and magnitude of this Reynolds stress. In §4.5, a more detailed analysis of the phase relationship of the components of the velocity of the oscillation will be given, and the magnitude and direction of the Reynolds stress will be obtained. It will be shown that this stress is generally favourable to the conversion of energy into the disturbance motion.

Thus, the two cases treated above are not only examples of the stability problems of basic flows which are exact solutions of the Navier–Stokes equations. They also embody several general physical aspects of the problems of hydrodynamic stability. The contrast between parallel flows and curved flows is clearly demonstrated.

A very illuminating case is the stability of the flow through a curved channel, studied by Dean (1928). Dean examined the stability of this flow with respect to disturbances of the type found in rotating cylinders. If $2h$ and a denote respectively the distance between the walls and the radius of the inner wall, then Dean found, for small values of h/a, a critical Reynolds number given by $2W_m h/\nu = 25 \cdot 45 (a/h)^{\frac{1}{2}}$, where W_m is the mean speed of flow. For greater Reynolds numbers the system is unstable, the instability first manifesting itself in a disturbance of the nature of a secondary flow. Now, for a straight channel, the critical Reynolds number is $3W_m h/\nu = 10,600$. Thus, even with $a/h = 10^4$—a very small curvature—Dean's critical Reynolds number would be 2545, far below 10^4, and the secondary flow would set in far earlier than the disturbance calculated for the case of plane Poiseuille motion. However, it is not clear yet which type of motion would induce transition to turbulence, because it might be anticipated from Taylor's experiments with rotating cylinders that a stationary secondary flow would persist when Dean's stability limit is barely exceeded.

Such conjectures are qualitatively borne out by experiments in curved pipes. When secondary flow begins to develop, there is no appreciable change in the loss of head. On the other hand, when turbulence appears in a straight pipe, there is a sudden increase in the loss.†

† See Goldstein (1937) for the detailed discussion of a case where pressure drop experiments do not show the first onset of instability.

4.2. Instability of revolving fluids

The instability of revolving fluids, with special reference to the stability of motion between rotating cylinders, has been treated by Lord Rayleigh (1916) in a very illuminating manner, neglecting the effect of viscosity. Rayleigh considered a disturbance with rotational symmetry and noted that the angular momentum of a fluid element would remain unchanged, according to Kelvin's circulation theorem. The motion along the radial and axial directions may then be treated as if the circulatory motion were absent, except for the presence of a centrifugal force of the magnitude v^2/r at a distance r from the axis, where v is the circulatory speed. Since $vr = k$, a constant, the centrifugal force is k^2/r^3, which is a known function of position for a given fluid element. We may then associate with each fluid element a 'potential energy' $\rho k^2/2r^2$. This is then analogous to the problem of a heterogeneous fluid in a field with potential energy proportional to r^{-2}. The equilibrium is stable only if the potential energy is a minimum; that is, the heavier fluids are in regions of lower potential energy. In the present case, this means that k^2 must be monotonically increasing outwards.

The potential energy $\rho k^2/2r^2$ is clearly the kinetic energy of circulatory motion $\frac{1}{2}\rho v^2$. Indeed, Rayleigh also gave a direct argument in terms of the kinetic energy. The kinetic energy associated with a given fluid ring at a distance r from the axis is proportional to

$$\frac{\rho v^2}{2} r \, dr = \frac{\rho}{4} \frac{k^2}{r^2} d(r^2). \qquad (4.2.1)$$

Suppose now that two rings of fluid, one with $k = k_1$ and $r = r_1$, and the other with $k = k_2$ and $r = r_2$, where $r_2 > r_1$, and of equal areas $(r_1 dr_1 = r_2 dr_2)$, are interchanged. The corresponding increment in kinetic energy is proportional to

$$(k_2^2/r_1^2 + k_1^2/r_2^2) - (k_1^2/r_1^2 + k_2^2/r_2^2) = (k_2^2 - k_1^2)(r_2^{-2} - r_1^{-2}), \qquad (4.2.2)$$

and is positive if $k_2^2 > k_1^2$, so that a circulation always increasing outwards makes the kinetic energy a minimum and thus ensures stability.

Von Kármán (1934) treated these ideas from the point of view of the pressure gradient. In the steady state, the centrifugal force

$\rho v^2/r$ must be balanced by the pressure gradient. If a ring of fluid at r_1 is displaced to r_2 (with $r_2 > r_1$), the centrifugal force $\rho v^2/r$ becomes $\rho(r_1 v_1/r_2)^2/r_2 = \rho(r_1 v_1)^2/r_2^3$. This is larger than the prevailing pressure gradient $\rho v_2^2/r_2$ if $(r_1 v_1)^2 > (r_2 v_2)^2$, or $k_1^2 > k_2^2$. In this case, the fluid element will continue its motion outwards, and the motion is unstable.

It is clear that the above discussion refers to the increase or decrease of the *square* of the circulation. For flow between cylinders rotating in opposite directions, the square of the circulation decreases from the inner cylinder to the point of zero speed, and increases outwards from there. Thus, instability of the motion is mainly associated with this inner region, where this disturbance is expected to be important. Such reasoning is very useful for the choice of approximation functions in the Galerkin method (Di Prima, 1955).

We may now complete the description of the mechanism of instability of the flow between rotating cylinders as follows: The viscous forces tend to produce an arrangement of circulation proportional to $Ar^2 + B$. If this arrangement is unstable, fluid elements with larger circulation (in absolute magnitude) will tend to move outwards, inducing a secondary flow. This tendency is retarded by viscous forces. If this latter effect is not strong enough, the rearrangement will occur. At the same time, the moving solid surfaces will tend to re-establish the original arrangement. A steady secondary flow is thus maintained.

Synge (1933) has derived Rayleigh's conclusion by a very simple mathematical reasoning. Let us return to equations (2.1.5) and consider the formal limit $R \to \infty$. Then we obtain, after eliminating $\hat{u}$

$$\frac{d}{dr}\left(\frac{1}{r}\frac{dg}{dr}\right) - \lambda^2\left(\frac{1}{\sigma^2}\frac{F}{r} + \frac{1}{r}\right)g = 0, \qquad (4.2.3)$$

where

$$g = r\hat{v}, \qquad F = \frac{1}{r^3}\frac{d}{dr}(\omega r^2)^2. \qquad (4.2.4)$$

The boundary conditions reduce to

$$g = 0 \quad \text{for} \quad r = 1 \quad \text{and for} \quad r = R_2/R_1. \qquad (4.2.5)$$

For given λ, this may be regarded as a characteristic equation for the determination of σ. But it is known from the general theory of the Sturm–Liouville equation† that, since

$$\frac{1}{r} > 0, \quad \frac{\lambda^2}{r} > 0, \qquad (4.2.6)$$

the characteristic values of σ^2 are necessarily real. Furthermore, if

$$F > 0 \quad \text{for} \quad 1 < r < r_2 = R_2/R_1, \qquad (4.2.7)$$

the values of σ^2 are negative; hence σ is pure imaginary, and the oscillation is neutrally stable. On the other hand, if

$$F < 0 \quad \text{for} \quad 1 < r < r_2 = R_2/R_1, \qquad (4.2.8)$$

then σ^2 is positive, and one of the two real roots gives instability. If F changes sign in the range, it is known that there exist both positive and negative characteristic numbers σ^2 and hence there is instability. Thus, the necessary and sufficient condition for stability is

$$\frac{d}{dr}(\omega r^2)^2 > 0, \qquad (4.2.9)$$

that is, that the square of the circulation $2\pi\omega r^2$ at a distance r should increase outwards, in agreement with above. Synge also generalized the condition to the case of heterogeneous fluids.

The condition (4.2.9) implies that the cylinders are rotating in the same direction and that

$$\Omega_2 R_2^2 > \Omega_1 R_1^2,$$

which has been shown by Synge (1938a) to be a sufficient condition for stability in a viscous fluid. In fact, with viscosity included, all the solutions are damped even for

$$\Omega_2 R_2^2 = \Omega_1 R_1^2,$$

---

† Consider the equation

$$\frac{d}{dx}\left\{k(x)\frac{dy}{dx}\right\} + \{\lambda m(x) - l(x)\}\, y = 0$$

with the boundary conditions

$$y(x_1) = y(x_2) = 0.$$

If throughout the range (x_1, x_2) we have

$$k(x) > 0, \quad l(x) \geqslant 0,$$

then all the characteristic numbers λ are real. Further, if $m(x)$ has one sign in the range, then λ has that sign. If $m(x)$ changes sign in the range, then there are positive and negative values of λ.

which would mark the threshold of stability in the inviscid case. Thus, clearly the effect of viscosity is to damp out the disturbances. The physical mechanism of instability may be described in the manner given by Rayleigh, subject to some damping effect of viscosity.

4.3. Instability of parallel flows

The instability of parallel flows has been treated by Lord Rayleigh in the (apparent) absence of viscous forces. Strictly speaking, a parallel flow must have a parabolic velocity distribution. However, there are many nearly parallel flows—flows of the type of the boundary layer—which have a variety of velocity distributions.[†] It should also be remarked that, in an inviscid fluid, any parallel flow is a possible solution.

If the instability problem is now formulated as in the case of plane Poiseuille motion, the amplitude function for the small disturbance satisfies the differential equation

$$(\bar{u}-c)(\phi''-\alpha^2\phi)-\bar{u}''\phi=0. \tag{4.3.1}$$

The boundary conditions are $\phi=0$ at the solid boundaries.

One observes immediately that the equation (4.3.1) has a singular point at $\bar{u}=c$. For neutral disturbances, this singular point could actually correspond to a layer of fluid between the walls, and complications may be expected. On the other hand, if c is complex, no such difficulty would be apparent since the equation is regular for *real* values of y. However, a solution of (4.3.1) is physically significant only if it represents an asymptotic limit of the complete viscous equation (3.2.5) of Orr and Sommerfeld. Detailed examinations of this mathematical problem (see Chapter 8) reveal that this is the case for real values of y only for self-excited disturbances. We can, indeed, study amplified disturbances by means of (4.3.1) without much difficulty and treat the neutral case in the limit $c_i \to 0$. Some of the important results in these cases will be outlined in this section; an indication of the difficulty in the damped case will be given towards the end.

One can show immediately that *if self-excited disturbances exist*,

---

† Whether the theory of parallel flows can be applied without modification is sometimes a delicate problem. It will be taken up when the occasion arises.

then $\bar{u}''(y)$ must vanish somewhere between the walls $y = y_1$ and $y = y_2$. Indeed, if $c_i > 0$, we may write (4.3.1) in the form

$$\phi'' - \alpha^2 \phi - \frac{\bar{u}''}{\bar{u} - c} \phi = 0. \tag{4.3.2}$$

If we now multiply (4.3.2) by ϕ^*, the complex conjugate of $\phi(y)$, and integrate between the limits, we obtain

$$\int_{y_1}^{y_2} \{|\phi'|^2 + \alpha^2 |\phi|^2\}\, dy + \int_{y_1}^{y_2} \frac{\bar{u}''}{\bar{u} - c} |\phi|^2\, dy = 0. \tag{4.3.3}$$

The vanishing of the imaginary part requires that

$$\int_{y_1}^{y_2} \frac{\bar{u}''}{|\bar{u} - c|^2} |\phi|^2\, dy = 0, \tag{4.3.4}$$

which can be satisfied only if $\bar{u}'' = 0$ somewhere in the interval (y_1, y_2).

The above result was first obtained by Lord Rayleigh in 1880, and points to the importance of the point of inflexion. Thus, if the velocity profile does not have a point of inflexion, for example, as in the case of plane Poiseuille motion, the flow should be stable in the absence of viscous forces.

If one further conjectures that viscous forces are stabilizing, one would arrive at the conclusion that plane Poiseuille motion is indeed stable, in contradiction with the results calculated in Chapter 3. One is therefore forced to conjecture that *viscous forces can be a cause of instability*. This point will be examined further in § 4.6.

The significance of the point of inflexion in the velocity profile is further enhanced by the following theorem of Tollmien (1935 b), which is in effect the converse of Rayleigh's: *For symmetrical velocity distributions, or velocity distributions of the type of the boundary layer, the condition $\bar{u}''(y) = 0$ implies instability.* For other profiles, this condition need not be sufficient.†

Tollmien's proof of his theorem is based on the establishment of a neutral oscillation and a perturbation therefrom. For the neutral oscillation, equation (4.3.2) immediately suggests the consideration of the case $c = c_s$, where c_s is the value of $\bar{u}$ at the point of inflexion. Then the singularity in (4.3.2) disappears. Further details of the

† For a counter example, see Lin (1945), p. 222.

proof will be given in Chapter 8, where other discussions of the stability of parallel flows in an inviscid fluid will also be given.

An examination of the Reynolds stress $-\rho\overline{u'v'}$ (where the bar denotes averaging with respect to x) of the disturbance is particularly illuminating. In the case of self-excited disturbances, Foote and Lin (1950) found that the rate of its change across the flow is given by[†]

$$\frac{\mathrm{d}\tau}{\mathrm{d}y} = \frac{1}{\alpha}\rho\overline{v^2}\frac{c_i\bar{u}''}{|\bar{u}-c|^2}, \qquad (4.3.5)$$

where v is the y-component of the velocity disturbance. In the limit $c_i \to 0$, this reduces to an earlier result of Tollmien for the neutral case: the Reynolds stress τ remains constant except for a discontinuity of the extent

$$[\tau] = \tau(y_c+0) - \tau(y_c-0) = \frac{\pi}{\alpha}\rho\overline{v^2}.\bar{u}_c''/|\bar{u}_c'|, \qquad (4.3.6)$$

at the critical point, where the subscript $(\ )_c$ denotes values at the critical point y_c, where $\bar{u}=c$.

At a solid boundary, $\tau=0$. Thus, if a neutral disturbance does exist, the total extent of the jump must vanish. If there is only one point y_c where $\bar{u}=c$, one is then led to the conclusion $\bar{u}''=0$ or $v_c=0$. In the former case, $\tau=0$ throughout. The latter possibility can be easily ruled out by a special investigation.

Foote and Lin (1950) worked out the distribution of Reynolds stress τ for symmetrical and asymmetrical jets (see figs. 4.1 and 4.2). Note that the rate of work done by the Reynolds stress,

$$P = \int \tau \frac{\mathrm{d}\bar{u}}{\mathrm{d}y}\mathrm{d}y, \qquad (4.3.7)$$

is positive in the case of self-excited disturbances[‡] and is equal to zero in the case of neutral disturbances even though τ does not vanish identically in the asymmetrical case. In the latter case, the value of c must be such that the jumps at y_s and y_t cancel out each other.

We have so far refrained from investigating the inviscid equation from a comprehensive point of view. In particular, no mention

---

[†] The original formula is expressed in terms of a function $g(y)$ which reduce to $-\bar{u}''(y)$ in the present case. For a derivation based directly on physical quantities, see Lin (1954b). For a mathematical derivation, see p. 120.

[‡] See § 4.5 for further discussions of the significance of this result.

has been made of damped disturbances. Now if equation (4.3.1) refers to a self-excited disturbance, its complex conjugate represents an equation for a damped disturbance:†

$$(\bar{u}-c^*)(\phi^{*\prime\prime}-\alpha^2\phi^*)-\bar{u}^{\prime\prime}\phi^* = 0, \qquad (4.3.8)$$

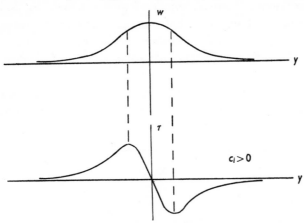

Fig. 4.1. Distribution of Reynolds stress caused by a self-excited oscillation in a symmetrical jet (after Foote and Lin, 1950).

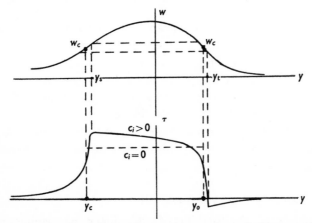

Fig. 4.2. Distribution of Reynolds stress in an asymmetrical jet, caused by neutral and self-excited oscillations (after Foote and Lin, 1950).

the amplitude function being $\phi^*(y)$. This observation has far-reaching consequences. If $\bar{u}^{\prime\prime} \neq 0$ we know, from Rayleigh's theorem, that self-excited disturbances do not exist. One might

† An asterisk at the *upper* right-hand corner denotes the complex conjugate.

conclude, at first sight, that damped disturbances are also impossible because their conjugates are self-excited disturbances. However, it seems plausible to conjecture that some disturbance of the wavy type is always possible for the physical system (though it is probably damped); that is, there is a solution for the complete Orr–Sommerfeld equation. Thus, one must conclude that *there are cases where a solution of the complete equation does not reduce, in the limit of infinite Reynolds number, to a solution of the inviscid equation in the whole interval* (y_1, y_2).

Actually, detailed investigation of the limiting process (see Chapter 8) shows that equation (4.3.1) *holds throughout the interval*

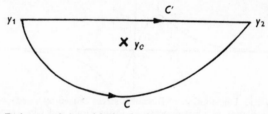

Fig. 4.3. Path around the critical point in the case $c_i < 0$ (after Lin, 1945).

(y_1, y_2), *only for self-excited disturbances.* For damped disturbances it has to be interpreted in the complex y-plane. If we take a path C from y_1 to y_2 in the complex y-plane, such that the point y_c (where $\bar{u} = c$) is enclosed by this path and the return path to y_1 along the real axis (see fig. 4.3), then the equation (4.3.1) holds along the path C for damped disturbances. Since y_c is in general a singular point of the equation, these two paths are not equivalent. If there is more than one singular point, each point has to be handled in a similar manner.

4.4. Vorticity theory of instability

The fact that the instability of a two-dimensional laminar flow is so closely related to the occurrence of a point of inflexion in the velocity profile suggests that there should be a simple physical interpretation. Since the basic equation for instability is essentially the vorticity equation, one would expect the point of inflexion to indicate a maximum or minimum of vorticity. The explanation along these lines, mentioned in §4.1, will now be given.

Since we are neglecting viscosity, a fluid element maintains its vorticity during a two-dimensional motion. From this point of view, a two-dimensional parallel flow may be regarded as the motion of a large number of vortex filaments under the action of each other. Filaments of equal vorticity are arranged in the same layer, and the whole field is built up of a collection of such layers.

Let us now consider the behaviour of a particular element of fluid having an excess of vorticity over that of the parallel shear flow.

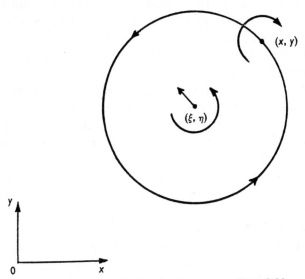

Fig. 4.4. Acceleration of vortices in a non-uniform field of vorticity ($\bar{\zeta}'(y) > 0$, $\Gamma > 0$) (after Lin, 1945).

Associated with this 'vortex', there is a distortion of the main vorticity distribution. Thus, if the vorticity gradient of the main flow is increasing in the direction of the positive y-axis, the fluid elements on the right of the vortex will be replaced, by this distortion, by those having a lower vorticity; those to the left, by elements having a higher vorticity (see fig. 4.4). This redistribution will induce an upward velocity at the 'vortex' as a little qualitative consideration will show. By detailed calculations, it can be shown that this results in an average acceleration of the 'vortex' given by (Lin, 1945)

$$a = \Gamma^{-1} \iint \{v'(x,y)\}^2 \, \bar{\zeta}'(y) \, dx \, dy \qquad (4.4.1)$$

in the direction of the positive y-axis, where Γ is the strength of the vortex (with conventional sign attached), $\bar{\zeta}'(y)$ is the gradient of vorticity of the main flow, and v' is the velocity in the y-direction due to the superposed 'vortex'.

Let us now imagine a disturbance of the parallel flow such that an element E_1 of fluid of the layer L_1 is interchanged with an element E_2 of a neighbouring layer L_2. For definiteness, let us suppose that the layer L_2 has a higher vorticity than the layer L_1 in the original undisturbed state. Since E_1 preserves its vorticity, it will appear to have a defect of vorticity when it is in layer L_2. Similarly, E_2 appears to have an excess of vorticity in layer L_1. Thus, both elements will have a tendency to move in accordance with the acceleration formula given above. By examining the signs of the various quantities in the acceleration formula, we can easily see that E_2 is accelerated toward a region of higher vorticity if the gradient of vorticity does not change sign anywhere in the fluid. Thus, E_2 is accelerated toward L_2. A similar consideration holds for the element E_1. Hence, in either case, *the fluid element is returned toward the layer where it belonged* (by its interaction with other vortex filaments). *The motion is therefore stable when the gradient of vorticity does not vanish.*

When there is an extremum of vorticity, an interchange of fluid elements on opposite sides of the extremum does not give rise to an excess or a defect of vorticity. Furthermore, the gradient of vorticity vanishes there, and has opposite signs on opposite sides of that layer. It can be easily seen from the above acceleration formula that the restoring tendency mentioned above is, even in the general case, largely impaired in such a case. Thus, exchanged fluid elements are not as strongly forced back by the action discussed above. An exchange of fluid elements constitutes a disturbance, because there is an exchange of momentum. Thus, a disturbance may tend to persist and perhaps to augment. The motion is not necessarily stable.

Another physical interpretation may be found specifically for periodic wavy disturbances. This is based on an observation of viscous forces on vorticity diffusion. The arguments will not be reproduced here (see Lin, 1945).[†]

[†] See also G. I. Taylor, *Phil. Trans.* A, **215**, 23–26 (1915) for a physical interpretation in terms of momentum considerations.

4.5. Energy balance in a disturbed flow

The transfer of energy between the basic flow and a superposed disturbance is a fundamental physical mechanism in turbulent motion as well as in the theory of instability of laminar motions. Such considerations were made by Reynolds (1895) and have been extensively used by many investigators ever since. For the study of the instability of laminar motion, we may mention in particular the discussions of Lorentz (1907), Orr (1907), von Kármán (1924) and Prandtl (1935). A more mathematical approach to these ideas is contained in the work of Synge (1938b) and Thomas (1942).

Such investigations are concerned with the conditions under which the energy of the disturbance decreases or increases with time. If possible, one would wish to avoid the solution of the differential equations of the small disturbance, which leads to such complicated mathematical analyses. This is usually accomplished by assuming a convenient pattern of the disturbance at a certain instant and then finding out whether the energy associated with it increases or decreases *immediately* afterwards. Since the pattern of the disturbance changes in the course of time, the energy could momentarily increase and subsequently die away. Thus, unless a flow is stable or unstable with respect to *all* disturbances, no conclusive answer can be expected.

In a viscous fluid, it can hardly be expected that motions at very small length scales are not damped out. Consequently, the energy method may be expected to give only criteria of stability. Even here only the *lower limit* for the critical Reynolds number can be expected, because stability must be established for all disturbances in the present method, while in reality only those satisfying the hydrodynamic equations need to be considered. The inclusion of the spurious disturbances would naturally require larger viscous damping to maintain the stability of the motion.

Investigations along this line in the references quoted above lead to Reynolds numbers which are substantially lower than those found by the more complete analysis of the small oscillations. Disturbances which increase very greatly initially and subsequently die away have also been found by Orr.†

† *Ibid.* pp. 90–4.

On the other hand, for the physical understanding of the instability of the flow, it is still important to examine the mechanism of energy balance. In particular, one has to find out how the viscous forces could help to augment the energy of the disturbance, as one is forced to expect after comparing the inviscid studies of Lord Rayleigh with the results obtained in the case of flow through the channel. It turns out that the key mechanism is a shift in the phase of the two components of the velocity of the oscillation by the viscous forces at the solid boundary. This produces a Reynolds stress which converts energy from the basic flow to the disturbance.

This conversion mechanism can be described by an equation of the form

$$\frac{\partial E}{\partial t} = \rho M - \mu N, \tag{4.5.1}$$

which can be easily derived from (1.2.10), for small two-dimensional periodic disturbances between two parallel walls. In the above equation, the symbols are defined as follows:

$$\left.\begin{aligned}
E &= \iint \frac{\rho}{2}(u'^2 + v'^2)\,dx\,dy, \\
\rho M &= -\rho \iint u'v' \frac{d\bar{u}}{dy}\,dx\,dy, \\
\mu N &= \mu \iint \zeta'^2\,dx\,dy, \quad \zeta' = v'_x - u'_y,
\end{aligned}\right\} \tag{4.5.2}$$

where the integration is taken over a fundamental rectangle with a width equal to one wavelength. Thus, the three terms in (4.5.1) represent respectively the rate of increase of the kinetic energy of the disturbance, the conversion of energy from the basic flow into the disturbance by a Reynolds shear $-\rho \overline{u'v'}$ (where the bar denotes average with respect to x), and the viscous dissipation. The relative magnitude of the two terms on the right-hand side of (4.5.1) determines whether the energy of the disturbance increases or decreases. Their ratio is

$$\frac{\rho M}{\mu N} = R \frac{M'}{N'}, \tag{4.5.3}$$

where R is the Reynolds number and M' and N' are the dimensionless forms of M and N.

The disturbance will die out if $RM'/N' < 1$, that is, if the Reynolds number is below the ratio N'/M'. The least value of N'/M' therefore gives a critical number R_c below which the motion is completely stable. This leads to a variational problem which has been considered by Orr (1907), Hamel (1911), von Kármán (1924) and others. If ψ' is the stream function, this leads to the characteristic-value problem

$$\Delta\Delta\psi' + \lambda[\bar{u}'(y)\,\psi'_{xy} + \bar{u}''(y)\,\psi'_x] = 0.$$

For periodic disturbances, Orr found the critical value to be 44·3 in the case of plane Couette motion. For motion through a channel, the value is 88, based on maximum velocity and half-width.†

The energy equation thus gives critical Reynolds numbers that are too low. It, however, still provides an important point of view for the understanding of the physical mechanism. Clearly, the viscous term in (4.5.1) always leads to a decrease of energy, and the increase is provided by the Reynolds stress $-\rho\overline{u'v'}$. It is also essential that this stress must have the same sign as the velocity gradient of the basic flow, if there is to be any instability.

We have seen that, for velocity profiles without a point of inflexion, instability must be due to the effect of viscosity. The energy equation then shows that the viscous forces must act in such a manner that a proper phase relationship is established between the u'- and the v'-components of the velocity. We shall now show‡ that if the disturbance is in the nature of a travelling wave, the viscous forces at the wall will always produce a *positive* stress in the following sense: the stress acting *on* the wall is in the direction of the travelling wave.

Consider first a periodic motion of the fluid along the wall, independent of the distance along it. In the absence of viscosity, a tangential velocity would be present at the wall. In the presence of viscosity, the fluid motion would tend to create a vorticity layer at the wall, which spreads out under the influence of the viscous forces. The distribution of vorticity is then given by the familiar formula

$$\zeta' = \mathrm{Re}\{e^{-i\omega t}e^{-(1-i)y/\delta_0}\}, \quad \delta_0 = (2\nu/\omega)^{\frac{1}{2}} \qquad (4.5.4)$$

† Synge (1938c) obtained the value 155 by vorticity considerations.
‡ The argument here follows Lin (1954b). See also Prandtl (1922). For a discussion of energy balance in the case of compressible fluids see Lees (1947), p. 18.

which is a solution of the diffusion equation

$$\frac{\partial \zeta'}{\partial t} = \nu \frac{\partial^2 \zeta'}{\partial y^2}.$$ (4.5.5)

In the case of a small disturbance from a basic flow, the vorticity distribution must satisfy the equation

$$\frac{\partial \zeta'}{\partial t} + \bar{u}\frac{\partial \zeta'}{\partial x} + v'\frac{d\bar{\zeta}}{dy} = \nu\left(\frac{\partial^2 \zeta'}{\partial x^2} + \frac{\partial^2 \zeta'}{\partial y^2}\right), \quad \bar{\zeta} = -\frac{d\bar{u}}{dy}.$$ (4.5.6)

Also, we would be interested in solutions containing the factor $\exp\{i(\alpha x - \omega t)\}$. However, near the wall, the terms in (4.5.6), which represent the convection of vorticity, are not important, because $\bar{u} = v' = 0$ at the wall. Also, if $\alpha\delta_0 \ll 1$, ζ'_{xx} must be negligible compared with ζ'_{yy}. Hence, a proper solution close to the wall is obtained by a slight modification of (4.5.4), that is,

$$\zeta' = \text{Re}\,\{e^{i(\alpha x - \omega t)}e^{-(1-i)y/\delta_0}\}.$$ (4.5.7)

At larger distances from the wall, the distribution of vorticity would be modified by the convection process.

By using (4.5.7), we can obtain the first terms of power-series developments for the components of velocity near the wall. This is done by using the equation of continuity and the definition of vorticity:

$$\left.\begin{aligned} u'_x + v'_y &= 0, \\ v'_x - u'_y &= \zeta'. \end{aligned}\right\}$$ (4.5.8)

Let the complex amplitudes for the two components of velocity be

$$\left.\begin{aligned} f(y) &= a_1 y + a_2 y^2 + a_3 y^3 + \ldots, \\ g(y) &= b_1 y + b_2 y^2 + b_3 y^3 + \ldots; \end{aligned}\right\}$$ (4.5.9)

then the equation of continuity shows that

$$b_1 = 0, \quad 2b_2 = i\alpha a_1, \quad 3b_3 = i\alpha a_2, \quad \ldots.$$ (4.5.10)

The Reynolds stress is given by $\tau = -(\frac{1}{2}\rho)\,\text{Re}\,(fg^*)$. (The asterisk denotes the complex conjugate.) Thus, a little calculation gives

$$\frac{\tau}{\rho \overline{v^2}} = -\frac{2}{3\alpha}\,\text{Re}(ia_2/a_1),$$

to the first approximation. By using (4.5.7), one can easily show that

$$\frac{a_2}{a_1} = -\frac{1-i}{2\delta_0}, \quad \mathrm{Re}\,(ia_2/a_1) = -\frac{1}{2\delta_0}. \qquad (4.5.11)$$

Thus,

$$\frac{\tau}{\rho v^2} = \frac{1}{3\alpha\delta_0} > 0. \qquad (4.5.12)$$

Thus, the stress always acts *on the wall in the direction of propagation of the disturbance wave.* For a wave propagating in the direction of

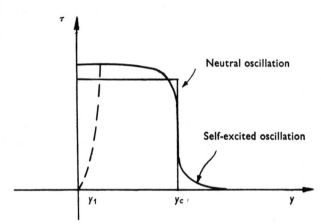

Fig. 4.5.   Distribution of Reynolds stress (dashed line gives influence of viscous forces).

the basic motion, the Reynolds stress produced is in favour of the conversion of the energy of the basic flow into the disturbance.

Fig. 4.5 shows the qualitative nature of the stress distribution, as obtained from a combination of the analysis of §4.3 and the result just reached. It is easily seen that the stress would give the correct qualitative nature for the energy transfer.

The relative phase relationships of the components $a_1, a_2, b_2, b_3, \ldots$ are shown in fig. 4.6, and it is seen that the resultant stress arises from a *difference* between the stresses produced by the correlation of a_1 with b_3 and that of a_2 with b_2. The difference between the factors 2 and 3 in (4.5.10) is responsible for the existence of a net Reynolds stress.

4.6. Oscillations of finite amplitudes

A complete theory of finite-amplitude oscillations about a basic flow would include the theory of fully developed turbulence, and is as yet far from being completely developed. However, certain general understanding has been reached, and details are available for some special cases. Some of these will be discussed in this section (see also §6.1).

One of the best methods of arriving at a general understanding of the physical process is the consideration of the energy relation. This

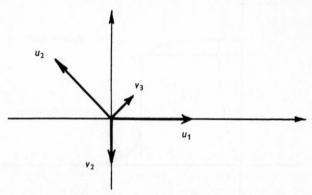

Fig. 4.6. Diagram showing the relative magnitude and phase of the various components of velocity.

was done in the previous section for infinitesimal disturbances. Although there are certain modifications necessary when finite disturbances are considered, the basic process is not different. Energy is converted from the basic flow to the disturbance by the action of the Reynolds stress and dissipated into heat by viscosity. To maintain a sustained oscillation, the Reynolds stress again must have the proper sign. Energy relations have been used very often for the study of fully developed turbulence, and the discussions are obviously applicable to finite disturbances of fairly general types.

One general conclusion has been obtained by Thomas (1942) from a consideration of the energy relation. For flow through a circular pipe, 'the pressure drop required to produce a given discharge is greater in the case of established turbulence [sustained oscillations] than for a steady [laminar] flow in the pipe'. This result may be anticipated from general physical considerations. However, since there has often been some confusion on the relation between the theories of finite and infinitesimal disturbances, the rigorous mathematical demonstration of such a result is very helpful. For example, we see immediately that if we impose the conditions that the pressure drop *and* the rate of discharge for the disturbed motion shall be the same as those for the laminar motion, we cannot expect to have a sustained oscillation. The instability calculated for the case of the channel† must be associated with an increased pressure drop of the second order. Such a pressure drop is beyond the scope of the linear theory, but it is by no means excluded.

The effect of finite amplitudes can also be traced through its influence on the velocity profile of the basic flow. Consider first the growth of an unstable disturbance from infinitesimal amplitudes. At first, the growth follows the linear theory. When the amplitude becomes considerable, a distortion of the basic flow results from the Reynolds stress associated with the disturbance. This distortion could strengthen the conversion of energy from the basic flow into the disturbance, leading to a quick transition to fully developed turbulence at sufficiently high Reynolds numbers of the basic flow.

The distortion of the basic flow by the disturbance suggests the possibility that a finite disturbance may exist at a Reynolds number lower than the critical one given by the linear theory. The modified velocity distribution could permit a type of oscillation which will die out in the basic flow. Meksyn and Stuart (1951) carried out such calculations for oscillations in the channel. The minimum critical Reynolds number is then obtained as a function of the amplitude of the oscillation (fig. 4.7). The results show a distinct lowering of the critical Reynolds number by an increase of the amplitude of the oscillation.‡

A related phenomenon is the well-known fact that fully developed turbulent motion can be maintained at very low Reynolds numbers —lower than those at which a stable laminar motion can also be

---

† Although the analysis of Thomas was given for the case of the pipe, similar discussions hold for the channel.

‡ The method of analysis used is such that the eventual rise of the critical Reynolds number cannot be relied upon.

maintained. Thus, in the case of pressure flow through the circular pipe, turbulent flow will die out only when the (diameter) Reynolds number is reduced below 2000, while laminar flow has been maintained up to a Reynolds number of the order of 5×10^4. Within these limits, transition to turbulence occurs at lower and lower Reynolds numbers when the residual disturbance in the flow is greater and greater.

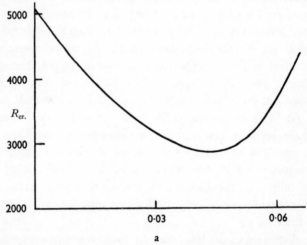

Fig. 4.7. Effect of the amplitude on the minimum critical Reynolds number for a possible neutral oscillation (after Meksyn and Stuart, 1951).

Since the mean flow that exists in a circular pipe under fully turbulent conditions is presumably stable with respect to small disturbances at a Reynolds number of, say, 3000, there does not seem to be an obvious correlation between the existence of turbulent flow at such Reynolds numbers and the kind of mechanism studied by Meksyn and Stuart. On the other hand, the instability of the laminar parabolic flow in a pipe, which has never been found on the basis of the linear theory, for any Reynolds number, could conceivably be attributed to such a process.[†] In this case we are interested in a small deviation from the parabolic velocity distribution, which is of course very different from that in fully developed turbulence.

[†] Another explanation of the instability of pipe flow has been given by Tatsumi (1952a) in terms of the linear theory applied to the entry region (cf. § 6.3).

CHAPTER 5

BOUNDARY LAYER OVER A FLAT PLATE

5.1. A brief survey of known results

The stability of the boundary layer formed by the flow over a flat plate is of practical as well as basic importance. In the incompressible case, its instability was first predicted by Tollmien (1929), who treated the problem as that of a parallel motion. Schlichting (1933a, b, 1935a) carried out a detailed calculation of the characteristics of the oscillations arising from the instability. Since the boundary layer grows in thickness in the downstream direction, Taylor (1938) questioned, on physical grounds, the validity of the application of theory of parallel flows. These doubts were removed by the experimental work of Schubauer and Skramstad (1947). Their results confirm all the general characteristics predicted by the theory. Schlichting's calculations, however, are only in qualitative agreement with the experiments. By adapting the procedure of Chapter 3 to this case,† Lin (1944) reproduced Tollmien's neutral curve, which is in better agreement with the experiments than Schlichting's later calculation. Following the same procedure used by Lin, Shen (1954) repeated the calculations of the rate of amplification and obtained results in closer agreement with experiments than Schlichting's values (figs. 5.1, 5.2a and 5.2b). Schlichting also calculated the amplitude distribution of the oscillations, which were found by Schubauer and Skramstad to be in general agreement with their experimental measurements (fig. 5.3).

The theory of stability of the boundary layer has been generalized to the case of an ideal gas, first considering only two-dimensional disturbances (Lees and Lin, 1946; Lees, 1947), then including three-dimensional disturbances (Dunn and Lin, 1952, 1953, 1955). Although the approach to the problem remains similar to the incompressible case, the actual development of the theory

† As far as the procedure of calculation goes, the main difference between the methods of Heisenberg and Tollmien lies in the treatment of the 'inviscid solutions'. While Heisenberg used power series in α^2, Tollmien used power series in $y - y_c$, where y_c is the critical point. The more subtle points in the mathematical theory will be discussed in Chapter 8.

reveals several important differences. We shall now briefly discuss some of these points, leaving the detailed treatment to the following sections. Naturally, the theory for the compressible case can be specialized to the incompressible case, and this will be carried out in § 5.3.

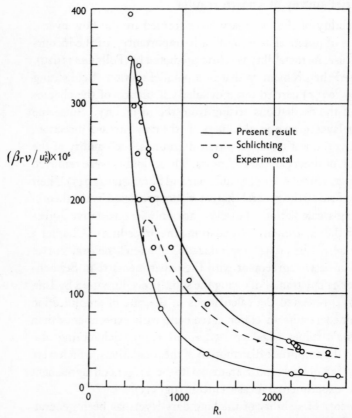

Fig. 5.1. Curve of neutral stability for Blasius flow (after Shen, 1954).

(i) One of the general conclusions reached by Lees and Lin is that, for subsonic and low supersonic Mach numbers, the stability characteristics are not sensitive to the boundary conditions on the temperature variations. Changing the boundary condition at the wall influences the stability characteristics only through the changes in the basic distributions of velocity, temperature and density. Such a conclusion is applicable also in the incompressible case. However,

Dunn and Lin (1955) found that such a conclusion is in general
no longer valid for moderately high supersonic Mach numbers.

(ii) It is found (Dunn and Lin, 1952) that Squire's theorem (see
Chapter 3) does not hold for three-dimensional disturbance in a
compressible fluid, although *mathematical* transformations similar
to those in the incompressible case can be made. The main reason
for this difference is the fact that the basic flow in the compressible
case involves not only the distribution of velocity but also those of
temperature and density. As we shall see below (§5.2), Squire's
conclusion in the incompressible case can be very simply derived by
a rotation of axes. It is clear that a vector quantity like velocity and

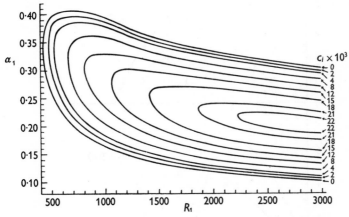

Fig. 5.2. (*a*) Amplification rates of Blasius flow (after Shen, 1954).

a scalar quantity like temperature do not behave in the same manner
during such a transformation. The interpretation of the final results
then becomes more complicated than in the incompressible case,
where distributions of scalar quantities are not involved.

(iii) Another important difference between the compressible
and the incompressible case is the following: Consider the disturbance in the free stream. In the incompressible case, if the disturbance is periodic in the direction of the stream, it must have an
exponential behaviour in the normal direction. If the disturbance
is to be bounded at infinite distance from the boundary, its amplitude must then decrease exponentially with the distance. On the
other hand, in a compressible fluid, since the speed of sound is

finite, a wavy disturbance can travel at supersonic speeds relative to the free stream. One would then expect the disturbance outside the boundary layer to be a wave with non-diminishing amplitude at

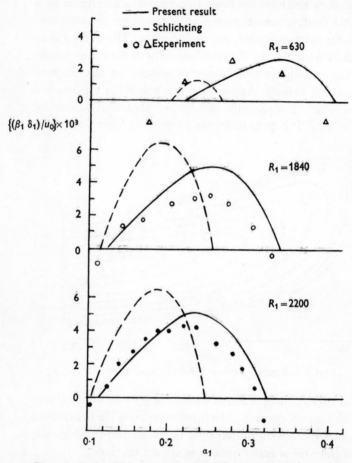

Fig. 5.2. (b) Amplification rates of Blasius flow, comparison with experiments (after Shen, 1954).

infinity instead of an exponential decay of the amplitude.† There is no discrete characteristic value problem for such disturbances unless some proper restriction is imposed. In fact, these 'supersonic disturbances' have not yet been fully studied.

† The contrast between these two cases is exactly the same as that between supersonic and subsonic steady flows past a wavy wall.

In all the existing theoretical analyses of the stability of the boundary layer in a gas, supersonic disturbances are assumed to be insignificant. This is based on the conjecture that the energy associated with such disturbances would propagate from the boundary layer in the nature of acoustic waves. Additional theoretical work and experimental evidence on this point are highly desirable.

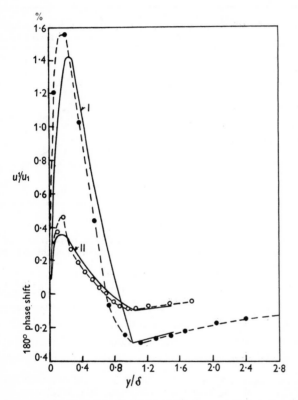

Fig. 5.3. Distribution of amplitude of oscillations across boundary layer. Solid curves are theoretical; points and dashed curve are experimental (after Schubauer and Skramstad, 1947).

(iv) Accepting the validity of this conjecture, Lees (1947) showed that, in many cases with a supersonic free stream, *two-dimensional* disturbances can be completely stabilized by cooling the solid boundary sufficiently. Calculations of the critical temperature ratios were made by Lees (1947), Bloom (1951) and

Van Driest (1951, 1952). Fig. 5.4† shows the critical ratio between temperatures at the wall and in the free stream at various free-stream Mach numbers. A wall temperature below this critical value would indicate stability with respect to two-dimensional disturbances. Fig. 5.5 shows some neutral curves calculated by Lees for two-dimensional disturbances in a number of cases.‡

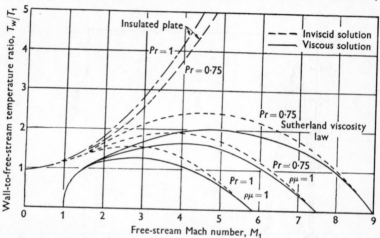

Fig. 5.4. Cooling required for complete stabilization of two-dimensional disturbances in the laminar boundary layer according to the inviscid and viscous fluid theory (after Van Driest, 1952).

However, if three-dimensional disturbances are also considered, one may still get a relatively low instability Reynolds number when two-dimensional disturbances are completely stabilized. Calculations were made by Dunn and Lin (1953) for such a case. At a free-stream Mach number of 1·6, the critical

† Bloom's values seem to be the first correct ones published. The figure is from Van Driest. In this figure and the various figures quoted below, the results have been obtained with somewhat different approximations for the properties of the gas. Lees assumed Prandtl number $\sigma = 1$ and $\rho\mu = $ constant, the constant being given by the value in the free stream. Dunn and Lin assumed $\sigma = 1$ and $\rho\mu = $ constant, the constant being given by the value at the wall. Van Driest used various combinations of $\sigma = 0.75$, $\sigma = 1$ and viscosity either proportional to the temperature or following Sutherland's law.

‡ A historical remark is in order here. Lees first computed the critical temperature ratios for complete stabilization, but there were unfortunately some errors in the numerical results (Lees, 1951), which were removed in the later calculations by Bloom and Van Driest cited above. All these authors used the same method. A later calculation by Bloom (1954) gave incorrect results because of the inadequacy of his formula for the parameter λ.

73

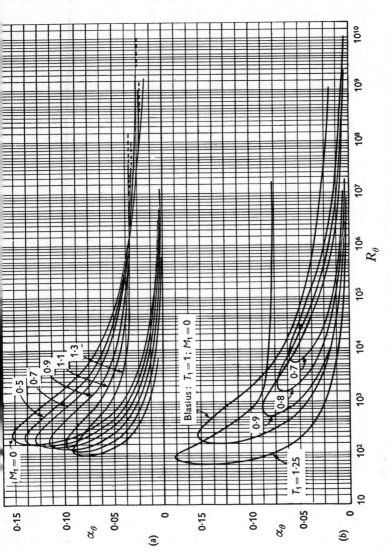

Fig. 5.5. Curves of neutral stability for two-dimensional disturbances in the boundary layer in a gas: (a) Insulated surface. (b) Surface at prescribed temperature (after Lees, 1947).

temperature ratio for complete stabilization of two-dimensional disturbances was found to be 1·073. For this temperature ratio, the neutral curves for several three-dimensional disturbances are shown in fig. 5.6, and the instability Reynolds number R_{xc} for these oblique waves, based on the distance downstream, is shown in fig. 5.7. However, Dunn and Lin also found that a moderate additional reduction of wall temperature is sufficient to increase the critical Reynolds number of all the three-dimensional disturbances to such

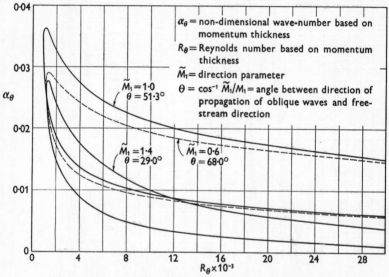

Fig. 5.6. Curves of neutral stability at a free-stream Mach number of $M_1 = 1 \cdot 6$ and a ratio of wall-to-free-stream temperature of $T_w/T_1 = 1 \cdot 073$.

large values that they presumably become of no practical significance. Thus, although there are always some unstable three-dimensional disturbances at sufficiently large Reynolds numbers, no matter how low the surface temperature may be, cooling still remains an effective method for stabilizing the boundary layer for moderate supersonic Mach numbers.†

Dunn and Lin also found that, under ordinary circumstances (for example, excepting rather extreme cooling), three-dimensional disturbances are not as important as two-dimensional disturbances for all subsonic Mach numbers.

† For general experimental support of complete stabilization, see J. Sternberg, *J. Aero. Sci.* **19**, 721–33 (1952).

5.2. Small disturbances in the boundary layer in a gas

The theory of small oscillations of the boundary layer will now be developed for an ideal gas. Let the motion and the thermodynamic state of the gas be characterized by

$$
\left.
\begin{aligned}
u_i &= \bar{u}_i + u_i' \quad (i = 1, 2, 3), \\
\Pi &= \bar{\Pi} + \Pi', \\
\rho_* &= \bar{\rho}_* + \rho_*', \\
\Theta &= \bar{\Theta} + \Theta',
\end{aligned}
\right\}
\tag{5.2.1}
$$

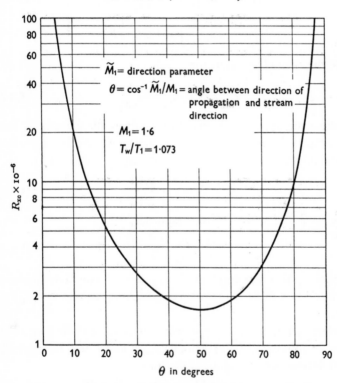

Fig. 5.7. Minimum critical Reynolds number *versus* direction of propagation of oblique waves.

as functions of the positional coordinates x_i $(i = 1, 2, 3)$, and the time τ. Suppose that the basic flow is the boundary layer over a semi-infinite flat plate, with the free stream not necessarily perpendicular to the leading edge. Then it can be shown, by careful examination of all the terms in the first-order disturbance equations of continuity, motion and energy, that *the basic flow may be treated as essentially parallel.* The analysis is fairly complicated, but the conclusion has been justified.[†] Thus, we may treat all the quantities associated with the basic flow as functions of x_2, the normal distance from the flat plate. The equations of the first order then become

$$\left.\begin{array}{l} \mathscr{D}\rho'_* + u'_2 \dfrac{d\bar{\rho}_*}{dx_2} = -\bar{\rho}_* \Delta', \\[2mm] \bar{\rho}_* \left(\mathscr{D}u'_i + u'_2 \dfrac{d\bar{u}_i}{dx_2} \right) = -\dfrac{\partial \Pi'}{\partial x_i} + \overline{\mu_*} \dfrac{\partial^2 u'_i}{\partial x_2^2}, \\[2mm] \bar{\rho}_* C_v \left(\mathscr{D}\Theta' + u'_2 \dfrac{d\overline{\Theta}}{dx_2} \right) = -\overline{\Pi}\Delta' + \overline{k_*} \dfrac{\partial^2 \Theta'}{\partial x_2^2}, \end{array}\right\} \qquad (5.2.2)$$

where the symbol $\mathscr{D}$ stands for

$$\mathscr{D} = \frac{\partial}{\partial \tau} + \bar{u}_1 \frac{\partial}{\partial x_1} + \bar{u}_3 \frac{\partial}{\partial x_3}, \qquad (5.2.3)$$

and the symbols c_v, $\overline{\mu_*}$, $\overline{k_*}$ stand respectively for the specific heat at constant volume, the viscosity coefficient for the basic motion, and the thermal conductivity. The quantity Δ' is defined by

$$\Delta' = \frac{\partial u'_1}{\partial x_1} + \frac{\partial u'_2}{\partial x_2} + \frac{\partial u'_3}{\partial x_3}. \qquad (5.2.4)$$

The equation of state is, to the first order,

$$\frac{\Pi'}{\overline{\Pi}} = \frac{\rho'_*}{\bar{\rho}_*} + \frac{\Theta'}{\overline{\Theta}}. \qquad (5.2.5)$$

We observe that the form of this system of equations remains *invariant* when there is a rotation of coordinate axes in the (x_1, x_3)-plane.

Periodic solutions of the equations for small disturbances. The system of equations (5.2.2) contains x_1, x_3 and τ only through the partial derivatives. Solutions of the form

$$q' = \hat{q}(x_2) \exp\{i(\alpha_1 x_1 + \alpha_3 x_3 - \alpha_1 c_1 \tau)\} \qquad (5.2.6)$$

are therefore expected. These are waves propagating in the (x_1, x_3)-plane in a direction specified by the numbers (α_1, α_3) (with the changing amplitude in time, if c_1 is complex).

Consider in particular the case $\alpha_3 = 0$. Then, the terms involving

† Cf., for example, Dunn's thesis (1953).

the x_3-derivatives drop out from the system of equations (5.2.2), and the equations for u_1', u_2', Π', ρ_*', Θ' are exactly the same as if the $\bar{u}_3$-component of the basic flow were absent. Thus, for waves propagating in the x_1-direction, only the $\bar{u}_1$-component of the basic flow (besides the distributions of the scalar quantities $\bar{\rho}_*$ and $\bar{\Theta}$) has any influence. Now, as remarked before, a rotation of the coordinate system in the (x_1, x_3)-plane will not change the form of the system of equations (5.2.2). Hence, by choosing the x_1-axis in the direction of wave propagation, we may conclude that for waves propagating in *any* direction only the component of the basic flow in *that* direction needs to be considered, together with the distributions of the scalar quantities $\bar{\rho}_*$ and $\bar{\Theta}$. *Every periodic three-dimensional disturbance may be treated in terms of a corresponding two-dimensional problem.* One need only take the proper component of velocity in the basic flow to carry out this simplification. The distributions of density and temperature are, however, the *same* for disturbances propagating in all directions.

In the above reduction of the three-dimensional problem to the two-dimensional case, no reference was made to the proper boundary conditions to be satisfied by the disturbances. The general physical nature of the boundary conditions will not be altered by the choice of the coordinate system, and hence they will not influence the above conclusions.

If we now reduce the above equations to the dimensionless form, it is clear that the waves propagating in the direction of the free stream would be associated with a Reynolds number R and a Mach number M, both defined in terms of the total velocity of the basic flow, while waves propagating at an angle χ relative to this direction would be associated with corresponding numbers

$$\left.\begin{array}{l} \tilde{R} = R\cos\chi, \\ \tilde{M} = M\cos\chi. \end{array}\right\} \tag{5.2.7}$$

For a given basic flow, each disturbance propagating in a given direction requires a new calculation with a corresponding Mach number of the free stream. The temperature and density distributions are to be left unchanged. In particular, if the dimensionless temperature distribution is expressed in terms of the Mach number of the free stream, the latter is not to be altered according to (5.2.7).

The above conclusions are valid under quite general circumstances. Whether the incoming stream is oblique or normal to the leading edge of the flat plate does not make any difference in our treatment. When specialized to the incompressible case, the above discussion covers both the original work of Squire (1933), and the case of oblique incoming flow discussed by Kuethe (1950). For two-dimensional parallel flows, Squire obtained a set of transformation formulae, which led to a conclusion equivalent to (5.2.7). Supplementary discussions are needed in Squire's method (see Pai, 1951). Kuethe, dealing with the case of the oblique incoming stream by using Squire's method, noted the variation of effective Reynolds number with different directions. He did not, however, arrive at the conclusion that the maximum effective Reynolds number is reached by waves propagating in the direction of the free stream.

5.3. Mathematical formulation of the stability problem

Consider now the stability of a two-dimensional boundary-layer flow over a flat plate which coincides with the (x_1, x_3)-plane. Let U_1 denote the free-stream velocity, and

$$\bar{u} = \bar{u}_1 / U_1 \qquad (5.3.1)$$

denote the dimensionless velocity distribution of the basic flow. The dimensionless temperature distribution will be denoted by

$$\bar{T} = \overline{\Theta} / \Theta_1, \qquad (5.3.2)$$

where Θ_1 is the temperature of the free stream. The Mach number M_1 of the free stream is given by

$$M_1^2 = U_1^2 / \gamma R_0 \Theta_1, \qquad (5.3.3)$$

where R_0 is the specific gas constant, and γ is the ratio of specific heats. The velocity and temperature distributions across the boundary layer depend on a number of factors, in particular, the boundary conditions at the wall and the free-stream Mach number M_1.

We consider a small two-dimensional disturbance of the boundary layer in the manner discussed previously. We introduce dimensionless variables as follows. For the coordinates we introduce

$$x, y, z = x_1/\delta, \ x_2/\delta, \ x_3/\delta, \qquad (5.3.4)$$

where δ is the *local* value of the boundary-layer thickness. The error introduced in neglecting its variation with x_1 and x_3 is generally of the same order as the parallel-flow approximation mentioned in §5.2. For the velocity components we use the free-stream speed as the reference quantity. Thus

$$\left.\begin{array}{l} u_1 = \bar{u}_1 + u_1' = U_1(\bar{u} + u'), \\ u_2 = \bar{u}_2 + u_2' = U_1(\bar{v} + v'). \end{array}\right\} \tag{5.3.5}$$

The dimensionless time is $\quad t = U_1 \tau / \delta.$ $\hspace{2cm}$ (5.3.6)

For pressure, density, temperature and the viscosity coefficient, we use the free-stream quantities as reference quantities:

$$\left.\begin{array}{l} \Pi = \Pi_1(\bar{p} + p'), \\ \rho_* = \rho_{*1}(\bar{\rho} + \rho'), \\ \Theta = \Theta_1(\bar{T} + T'), \\ \mu_* = \mu_{*1}(\bar{\mu} + \mu'). \end{array}\right\} \tag{5.3.7}$$

For the representation of periodic solutions, we use the following system of notation:

$$\left.\begin{array}{l} u' = \hat{u}(y) \exp\{i\alpha(x - ct)\}, \\ v' = \hat{v}(y) \exp\{i\alpha(x - ct)\}, \\ p' = \hat{p}(y) \exp\{i\alpha(x - ct)\}, \\ \rho' = \hat{\rho}(y) \exp\{i\alpha(x - ct)\}, \\ T' = \hat{T}(y) \exp\{i\alpha(x - ct)\}. \end{array}\right\} \tag{5.3.8}$$

Substitution of these relations into (5.2.2) gives the following system of equations for the amplitude functions:

$$\left.\begin{array}{l} \bar{\rho}\{i\alpha(\bar{u} - c)\,\hat{u} + \bar{u}'\hat{u}\} = -\dfrac{i\alpha}{\gamma M_1^2}\hat{p} + \dfrac{\bar{\mu}}{R}\hat{u}'', \\[2ex] \bar{\rho}\{i\alpha(\bar{u} - c)\,\hat{v}\} \quad = -\dfrac{1}{\gamma M_1^2}\hat{p}' + \dfrac{\bar{\mu}}{R}\hat{v}'', \\[2ex] i\alpha(\bar{u} - c)\,\hat{\rho} + \bar{\rho}'\hat{v} + \bar{\rho}\{i\alpha\hat{u} + \hat{v}'\} = 0, \\[2ex] \bar{\rho}\{i\alpha(\bar{u} - c)\,\hat{T} + \bar{T}'\hat{v}\} = -(\gamma - 1)\bar{p}(i\alpha\hat{u} + \hat{v}') + \dfrac{\gamma\bar{\mu}}{\sigma R}\hat{T}''. \end{array}\right\} \tag{5.3.9}$$

This system of four equations for the five variables $\hat{u}$, $\hat{v}$, $\hat{p}$, $\hat{\rho}$, $\hat{T}$ will be supplemented by the equation of state:†

$$\frac{\hat{p}}{\bar{p}} + \frac{\hat{\rho}}{\bar{\rho}} = \frac{\hat{T}}{\bar{T}}. \tag{5.3.10}$$

† The bar in $\bar{T}$ shall be dropped after equation (5.3.10) for simplicity.

To see the analytical nature of the system of equations (5.3.9), it is convenient to introduce the variables

$$Z_1 = \hat{u}, \quad Z_2 = \hat{u}', \quad Z_3 = \hat{v}/\alpha,$$
$$Z_4 = \frac{\hat{p}}{M_1^2}, \quad Z_5 = \hat{T}, \quad Z_6 = \hat{T}'. \tag{5.3.11}$$

Then (5.3.9), together with (5.3.10), become a system of *six* equations of the first order. These equations, when reduced to the normal form, have coefficients analytic in the independent variable y, and the parameters M_1^2, αR, α^2 and c.

Six homogeneous boundary conditions must be satisfied for a natural oscillation. For an (ideally) insulated wall, these are

$$\hat{u}(0) = \hat{v}(0) = \hat{T}'(0) = 0,$$
$$\hat{u}, \hat{v}, \hat{T} \text{ bounded as } y \to \infty. \tag{5.3.12}$$

For a fixed wall temperature, the condition $\hat{T}'(0) = 0$ is replaced by $\hat{T}(0) = 0$. The boundedness of the disturbance at infinity often implies (case of 'subsonic disturbances')

$$\hat{u}, \hat{v}, \hat{T} \to 0 \quad \text{as} \quad y \to \infty. \tag{5.3.13}$$

In that case, the characteristic values are discrete, and are determined by a secular equation of the form

$$F(M_1^2, \alpha R, \alpha^2, c) = 0. \tag{5.3.14}$$

In other cases, the solution may have a wavy nature at infinity (case of 'supersonic disturbances'). Then the characteristic values are continuous.

In the discrete case, for an insulated wall,† the formula (5.3.14) for determining the characteristic values can be reduced to the following form:
$$E(\alpha, c, M_1^2) = F(z), \tag{5.3.15}$$

In this formula, $F(z)$ is the Tietjen's function (cf. (3.6.6))

$$F(z) = 1 + \int_{+\infty}^{-z} \zeta^{\frac{1}{2}} H_{\frac{1}{3}}^{(1)} [\tfrac{2}{3}(i\zeta)^{\frac{3}{2}}] \, d\zeta \Big/ z \int_{+\infty}^{-z} \zeta^{\frac{1}{2}} H_{\frac{1}{3}}^{(1)} [\tfrac{2}{3}(i\zeta)^{\frac{3}{2}}] \, d\zeta, \tag{5.3.16}$$

where
$$z = (\alpha R)^{\frac{1}{3}} \left[\frac{3}{2} \int_0^{y_c} \sqrt{\left(\frac{c - \bar{u}}{\nu} \right)} \, dy \right]^{\frac{2}{3}}. \tag{5.3.17}$$

---

† For other boundary conditions, the formula is in general more complicated. Obviously, the same formula (5.3.15) holds whenever the free stream has a Mach number low enough to make temperature boundary condition unimportant.

The function $E(\alpha, c, M_1^2)$ is given by

$$E = -i\left(\frac{\bar{u}-c}{\nu}\right)_w^{\frac{1}{3}}\left[\frac{3}{2}\int_0^{y_c}\sqrt{\left(\frac{c-\bar{u}}{\nu}\right)}\,dy\right]^{-1}\Phi(0)/\Psi'(0), \quad (5.3.18)$$

where the subscript ( )$_w$ denotes the values at the wall,

$$\Psi'(y) = i\{T\Phi' - M_1^2\bar{u}'(\bar{u}-c)\Phi\}\{T - M_1^2(\bar{u}-c)^2\}^{-1}, \quad (5.3.19)$$

and $\Phi(y)$ is a solution of the inviscid equation

$$\frac{d}{dy}\left\{\frac{(\bar{u}-c)\phi' - \bar{u}'\phi}{T - M_1^2(\bar{u}-c)^2}\right\} = \frac{\alpha^2(\bar{u}-c)}{T}\phi, \quad (5.3.20)$$

for $\phi = i\hat{v}/\alpha$, satisfying the condition,

$$\Phi(y) \to 0 \quad \text{as} \quad y \to \infty. \quad (5.3.21)$$

The functions Ψ' and Φ constitute a part of a particular inviscid solution of the system of equations (5.3.9), that is, a solution obtained after dropping terms multiplied by $1/R$ in these equations.

Let us, for the moment, restrict ourselves to neutral disturbances. For large y, (5.3.20) becomes

$$\frac{d^2\phi}{dy^2} = \beta^2\phi, \quad \beta^2 = \alpha^2\{1 - M_1^2(1-c)^2\}. \quad (5.3.22)$$

It is thus clear that for

$$c < 1 - 1/M_1, \quad (5.3.23)$$

the solution for $\phi(y)$ does not vanish at infinity. Such solutions represent sound waves associated with the boundary layer. They travel with a supersonic phase velocity relative to the free stream in the direction of flow. For neutral subsonic disturbances, with

$$c > 1 - 1/M_1, \quad (5.3.24)$$

one solution of (5.3.22) dies off exponentially with y. If β denotes the positive square root,

$$\beta = \alpha\sqrt{\{1 - M_1^2(1-c)^2\}} > 0, \quad (5.3.25)$$

the solution behaves as $e^{-\beta y}$, that is,

$$\frac{\phi'}{\phi} \to -\beta \quad \text{as} \quad y \to \infty. \quad (5.3.26)$$

We then have discrete characteristic values.

The principal difference between the above formulation and that given by Lees and Lin (1946) lies in the formula (5.3.17) for z and a factor in (5.3.18). The earlier form would be obtained by assuming c to be small and taking only the first term in the power-series expansion of $\bar{u}-c$ and ν. In the supersonic case, where c is not small, such an expansion does not represent a good approximation for many cases of interest.

An improvement can be made in the solution Φ so that it satisfies the original system (5.3.9) better than prescribed by (5.3.20). However, this is not found worth while for the purposes of evaluating the characteristic value problem.†

The incompressible case. The case of Blasius flow can be obtained from the above results by putting $M_1 = 0$ and $T = 1$. It can also be treated directly by using the Orr–Summerfeld equation and imposing the conditions

$$\left.\begin{array}{l} \phi(0) = \phi'(0) = 0, \\ \phi(y), \quad \phi'(y) \to 0 \quad \text{as} \quad y \to \infty. \end{array}\right\} \tag{5.3.27}$$

Equation (5.3.22), which holds for large values of y, reduces to

$$\phi'' - \alpha^2 \phi = 0, \tag{5.3.28}$$

and hence the solution $\phi(y)$ should behave as $e^{-\alpha y}$ in order to fulfil the conditions at infinity. Thus we have the condition

$$\frac{\phi'(y)}{\phi(y)} \to -\alpha \quad \text{as} \quad y \to \infty. \tag{5.3.29}$$

If $\Phi(y)$ is such a solution of the inviscid equation

$$(\bar{u} - c)(\phi'' - \alpha^2 \phi) - \bar{u}'' \phi = 0 \tag{5.3.30}$$

(to which (5.3.20) reduces in the present case), the formula for determining the characteristic values is again given by an equation of the form (5.3.15), with the definitions (5.3.16)–(5.3.18), and $M_1 = 0$. Again, the values of c are usually so small that we may reduce z and E to

$$z = (\alpha R \bar{u}'_c)^{\frac{1}{3}} (c/\bar{u}'_c), \tag{5.3.31}$$

$$E = -[\Phi(0)/\Phi'(0)](c/\bar{u}'_c). \tag{5.3.32}$$

These formulas may be compared with those in Chapter 3.

5.4. Methods for calculation of stability characteristics: some simplified formulas

In this section we shall describe the methods which are used for the actual calculation of the stability characteristics. For such purposes, it has been found convenient to impose the condition

---

† For the detailed discussions of such improved solutions in the incompressible case, see Chapter 8.

(5.3.26) at the edge of the boundary layer $x_2 = \delta$, or $y = 1$, since this condition is satisfied identically to a very good approximation for $y > 1$. However, even with this approximation the actual work is quite laborious, and often the assumption is made that α is small. Although most of the existing calculations are made on the basis of this assumption, it is by no means satisfactory for all cases. In fact, some of the existing calculations are made by using methods adequate only for reasonably small values of α even though the actual values of α obtained are fairly large. Adequate methods for dealing with such cases are still lacking and are very much to be desired.

Even with the simplification of small α the calculations for each case are fairly lengthy. We shall therefore postpone their discussion for the moment, and first present some simple useful results.

(i) *Estimation of minimum critical Reynolds number.* For many purposes, a knowledge of the minimum critical Reynolds number is quite adequate. For this reason, Lin (1945) devised a formula for estimating this minimum number in terms of quantities which can be easily computed. The original formula was devised for the incompressible case. With the introduction of further approximations, Lees (1947) was able to obtain a similar formula for the case of the compressible gas. In the incompressible case, the minimum critical Reynolds number is given by

$$R_1 = 25(\bar{u}'_w \delta_1)/c^4, \qquad (5.4.1)$$

where R_1 is the Reynolds number defined in terms of the displacement thickness and the free-stream speed, $\bar{u}'_w$ denotes the slope of the velocity profile at the wall, δ_1 the displacement thickness, both in dimensionless form, and c is the dimensionless wave speed determined from the condition

$$v(c) = -\pi \bar{u}'_w c(\bar{u}''_c/\bar{u}'^3_c) = 0.58. \qquad (5.4.2)$$

In this last formula, $\bar{u}'_c$ and $\bar{u}''_c$ are the values of $\bar{u}'(y)$ and $\bar{u}''(y)$ at the point where $\bar{u}(y) = c$. In the Blasius case, this estimate gives good agreement with the value obtained from detailed calculations. It is suggested for rough estimates of the critical Reynolds number for other flows of the boundary-layer type.†

† See Chapter 6 for some of the applications to various special cases.

The formula of Lees is

$$R_1 = \frac{25\bar{u}'_w \delta_1}{c^4} \frac{T_c^{1\cdot76}}{\sqrt{\{1 - M_1^2(1-c)^2\}}}, \tag{5.4.3}$$

with c determined by

$$v(c) = -\pi \frac{\bar{u}'_w c}{T_w} \left[\frac{T^2}{\bar{u}'^3} \frac{d}{dy} \left(\frac{\bar{u}'}{T} \right) \right]_{\bar{u}=c} = 0\cdot58, \tag{5.4.4}$$

where T_w is the temperature at the wall, T_c is the temperature at the point where $\bar{u} = c$, and M_1 is the free-stream Mach number. The other quantities have similar meanings.† In view of later work, it is clear that this formula is a useful approximation only in the subsonic case and low supersonic Mach numbers.

(ii) *Complete stabilization of two-dimensional disturbances.* Lees also found that two-dimensional disturbances can be completely stabilized by cooling the wall. Indeed, if the estimation formula (5.4.3) is accepted, it is seen that $R_1 \to \infty$ as $c \to (1 - 1/M_1)$. Hence, if

$$v(c) = 0\cdot58 \quad \text{for} \quad c = 1 - 1/M_1, \tag{5.4.5}$$

the boundary layer is completely stabilized. The function $v(c)$ is defined by (5.4.4) and depends on the basic flow, which in turn depends on the temperature at the wall. Thus, if we calculate $v(1 - 1/M_1)$ as a function of the wall temperature, the critical wall temperature is reached when (5.4.5) is fulfilled.

While the argument just given depends on the approximation formula (5.4.3), which is sometimes found to be rather crude, the result (5.4.5) is actually more dependable. It is also independent of the particular boundary condition of an insulated wall. A more detailed argument for this will be presented in § 5.6.

(iii) *Three-dimensional disturbances.* The above results can be applied to three-dimensional disturbances by means of the transformation (5.2.7). For other discussions of three-dimensional disturbances, see §§ 5.1 and 5.6.

---

† In the original formula of Lees, the equation $v = 0\cdot58$ is replaced by $v(1 - 2\lambda) = 0\cdot58$, where λ should be given by (5.5.2), according to Dunn and Lin (1955). There is as yet no known case where the value of λ is large, and hence λ can be ignored for the purposes of rough estimates. However, in the older form of the theory used by Lees, λ was given by a different formula; its value could be quite large, and it was therefore found desirable to include it. The older formula for λ is misleading and is not given anywhere in this monograph.

5.5. General relations for the calculation of stability characteristics

Let us now return to the basic formula (5.3.15) for the calculation of the characteristic values. After some reduction, this formula for calculation can be put into the form

$$\mathscr{F}(z) = (1+\lambda)\frac{u+iv}{1+\lambda(u+iv)}, \tag{5.5.1}$$

where $\mathscr{F}(z)$ is described in Chapter 3,

$$\lambda(c) = \frac{\bar{u}'_w}{c}\left(\frac{c}{\nu_w}\right)^{-\frac{1}{2}}\left[\frac{3}{2}\int_0^y \sqrt{\left(\frac{c-\bar{u}}{\nu}\right)}\,dy\right]^{\frac{2}{3}} - 1, \tag{5.5.2}$$

and

$$u+iv = 1 + \frac{\bar{u}'_w c}{T_w}\frac{\phi'_{22}+\beta\phi_{22}}{\phi'_{11}+\beta\phi_{12}}. \tag{5.5.3}$$

In the last formula, $\phi_1(y)$ and $\phi_2(y)$ denote two appropriate solutions of (5.3.20), and $\phi_{i\kappa} = \phi_i(y_\kappa)$, $\phi'_{i\kappa} = \phi'_i(y_\kappa)$ (with $i, \kappa = 1, 2$ and $y_1 = 0$, $y_2 = 1$). Explicitly, they are given by

$$\left.\begin{aligned}
\phi_{12} &= (1-c)\sum_{n=0}^{\infty}\alpha^{2n}H_{2n}(c),\\
\phi_{22} &= (1-c)\sum_{n=0}^{\infty}\alpha^{2n}K_{2n+1}(c),\\
\phi'_{12} &= (1-c)^{-1}[1-M_1^2(1-c)^2]\sum_{n=0}^{\infty}\alpha^{2n}H_{2n-1},\\
\phi'_{22} &= (1-c)^{-1}[1-M_1^2(1-c)^2]\sum_{n=1}^{\infty}\alpha^{2n}K_{2n}.
\end{aligned}\right\} \tag{5.5.4}$$

where the quantities H_n and K_n are the following definite integrals:

$$\left.\begin{aligned}
H_0 &= 1, \quad H_1 = \int_0^1\frac{(\bar{u}-c)^2}{T}\,dy,\\
H_2 &= \int_0^1\left\{\frac{T}{(\bar{u}-c)^2}-M_1^2\right\}dy\int_0^y\frac{(\bar{u}-c)^2}{T}\,dy,\\
H_3 &= \int_0^1\frac{(\bar{u}-c)^2}{T}\,dy\int_0^y\left\{\frac{T}{(\bar{u}-c)^2}-M_1^2\right\}dy\int_0^y\frac{(\bar{u}-c)^2}{T}\,dy,\\
&\cdots,
\end{aligned}\right\} \tag{5.5.5}$$

and

$$K_0 = 1, \quad K_1 = \int_0^1 \left\{ \frac{T}{(\bar{u}-c)^2} - M_1^2 \right\} dy,$$

$$K_2 = \int_0^1 \frac{(\bar{u}-c)^2}{T} dy \int_0^y \left\{ \frac{T}{(\bar{u}-c)^2} - M_1^2 \right\} dy,$$

$$K_3 = \int_0^1 \left\{ \frac{T}{(\bar{u}-c)^2} - M_1^2 \right\} dy \int_0^y \frac{(\bar{u}-c)^2}{T} dy \int_0^y \left\{ \frac{T}{(\bar{u}-c)^2} - M_1^2 \right\} dy,$$

....

The constant β is given by

$$\beta = \alpha \sqrt{\{1 - M_1^2(1-c)^2\}}. \tag{5.5.7}$$

The reduction of these formulae to the incompressible case is made by putting $M_1 = 0$ and $T = 1$.

Calculations based on the formulas (5.5.1) and (5.5.3) are still very elaborate. Often the assumption is made that α is small.

Approximation for small values of the wave number. If we neglect higher-order terms in (5.5.3), we obtain the following simplified form:

$$u + iv = \frac{\bar{u}_w' c}{T} \left\{ \left(K_1 + \frac{T}{\bar{u}_w' c} \right) + \frac{\sqrt{\{1 - M_1^2(1-c)^2\}}}{\alpha(1-c)^2} \right\}. \tag{5.5.8}$$

It is clear that if $u + iv$ is to remain finite as $\alpha \to 0$, we must have, at the same time, either one of the following conditions:

$$\left. \begin{array}{r} c \to 0, \\ \sqrt{\{1 - M_1^2(1-c)^2\}} \to 0. \end{array} \right\} \tag{5.5.9}$$

In such cases, the neglect of the higher powers of α is certainly justified.

The results described in § 5.1 are based on calculations made by the use of (5.5.8) or the retention of some terms of higher powers of α. It should be cautioned, however, that some of the results are given for reasonably large values of α. In those cases, only the qualitative trends shown can be relied upon. As mentioned before, better methods for dealing with large values of α are still lacking.

5.6. Stabilization of the boundary layer by cooling and other methods

If we restrict ourselves to two-dimensional subsonic disturbances, we have the essential restriction $c > 1 - 1/M_1$. It could happen that the equation (5.5.1) cannot be satisfied under this restriction. The reason is as follows. The imaginary part of $\mathscr{F}(z)$ has an upper limit. If it should happen that, for $c > 1 - 1/M_1$, the right-hand side of (5.5.1) has an imaginary part always above this upper limit (for all α), then two-dimensional subsonic disturbances are not possible. When such a situation occurs, the boundary layer is usually interpreted as being completely stabilized with respect to two-dimensional disturbances. This interpretation is plausible, but it has so far not yet been made conclusive, because of the uncertainty of the role of the supersonic disturbances. Nevertheless, it seems worth while to try to determine this critical condition for two-dimensional subsonic disturbances.

Clearly the condition $c > 1 - 1/M_1$ can be important only for a supersonic free stream (if $c > 0$, as is usually implied). Indeed, one often finds that, for ordinary supersonic Mach numbers, say 2 or 3, and for a cooled surface, the imaginary part of the right-hand side of (5.5.1) does exceed the maximum value 0·58 of $\mathscr{F}_i(z)$ for all $c > 1 - 1/M_1$. In fact, it is usually a monotonically increasing function of c. Thus, the critical condition is to be associated with $c = 1 - 1/M$.

Now, for α not large, (5.5.8) is a reasonable approximation for $u + iv$. As c approaches the value $1 - 1/M_1$, unless $\alpha \to 0$ at the same time, both the real *and* the imaginary parts of $u + iv$ would be determined, and equation (5.5.1) would not be satisfied in general.

Thus, the critical condition is given by $c = 1 - 1/M_1$ and $\alpha = 0$. In this case, the real part of (5.5.8) is left undetermined, but the imaginary part is fully determined. With this knowledge, equation (5.5.1) determines fully the value of z. Indeed, it is very easy to verify that the imaginary part is given by (5.5.4) with $c = 1 - 1/M_1$, provided λ is set equal to zero. The formula (5.4.5) then follows readily.

We may recall that all the above deductions were essentially based on the condition of an insulated boundary. Such a boundary condition is not realistic when the wall is being cooled. However, careful examination shows that the characteristic-value problem, in the limit $\alpha \to 0$, reduces to the same form as that for the case of an insulated wall. We should also note that in the limit $\alpha \to 0$, the approximate expression (5.5.8) is identical with the full expression (5.5.3). The conversion of equation (5.5.1) into more convenient forms will not be discussed here. (For details for both of the above points see Dunn and Lin (1955).)

When the above arguments are applied to three-dimensional disturbances, the restriction $c > 1 - 1/M_1$ becomes $c > 1 - 1/M_1 \cos \chi$, and is no stronger than $c > 0$ for $\chi > \cos^{-1}(1/M_1)$. Thus, the values of c may go down to zero, in this case. Since $v(c) = 0$ for $c = 0$, one may expect that there is always a class of three-dimensional disturbances. As mentioned in §5.1, these disturbances also become quite stable when the cooling of the wall is moderately more severe than that required for stabilizing the two-dimensional subsonic disturbances.

Note added in proof

Recently, John Laufer found oscillations in the supersonic boundary layer with frequency characteristics of the same nature as those computed from the stability theory.

CHAPTER 6

OTHER NEARLY PARALLEL FLOWS

6.1. Instability of the boundary layer and its transition to turbulence

In the previous chapter, the theory of the stability of the boundary layer has been developed. Although the basic flow discussed was that over a flat plate, the theory is directly applicable to other cases with different distributions of velocity, temperature and density. Some common factors influencing the basic flow are

(i) heating and cooling of the boundary,

(ii) pressure gradient,

(iii) suction or injection of fluid at the wall.

For a complete investigation of the stability characteristics, in the various cases, a great deal of numerical calculation has to be made. It is therefore desirable to have some rapid method of calculation, which will at least give a rough estimate of the influence of these factors. For such purposes, the approximation formulas given in §5.4 were derived.

Curvature of the boundary modifies the stability characteristics of the boundary layer in a different manner. It has been found theoretically by Görtler (1940a, b, 1941) and experimentally by Liepmann (1943, 1945) that, over a *concave* surface, the dominating type of disturbance is not that discussed in the previous chapter, but analogous to that studied by Taylor (1923) in the case of flow between rotating cylinders (see Chapter 3). Over a *convex* surface, instability of the former type prevails.

The influence of the various factors mentioned above will be treated in §6.2. We shall first give a brief discussion of the relation between the instability of the boundary layer and its transition to turbulence.

Transition to turbulence. From a practical standpoint, the transition of a laminar flow into turbulence is more important than the instability problem itself. Fig. 6.1 shows the transition Reynolds number obtained by Schubauer and Skramstad (1947) for the flow over a flat plate, as the turbulence level in the free stream is changed. It is clear that this number is well above the instability Reynolds number of 5×10^4 predicted by Tollmien. In fact, only at the lowest levels of turbulence in the free stream were Schauber and Skramstad able to observe the oscillations predicted by the instability theory.

One mechanism for transition may be traced to the amplification of the oscillations as they pass downstream. It has been suggested, on the basis of the general nature of turbulent motion, that there is

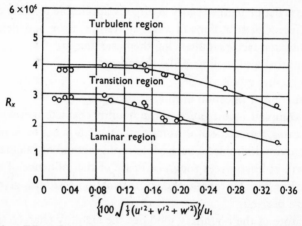

Fig. 6.1. Effect of turbulence on x-Reynolds number of transition. Flat plate, zero pressure gradient (after Schubauer and Skramstad, 1947).

a rapid development to transition when the amplitude of such oscillations becomes so high that the Reynolds stress associated with them becomes comparable to the shear in the basic flow. Attempts to estimate the transition Reynolds number along this line were made by Liepmann (1945) and by Lees (1952), with reasonable results.

However, in such an analysis there is always some difficulty in fixing the level of the turbulence in terms of sources of the disturbances. If, as in the experiments of Schubauer and Skramstad, there is a steady source upstream (a vibrating ribbon) one can easily conceive of a timewise periodic disturbance which increases in amplitude as it passes downstream. On the other hand, if the disturbance is caused by the turbulence in the free stream, one would expect forced oscillations due to this source. One may wish to match both the time and space frequencies of the disturbances inside the boundary layer with those in the turbulent motion outside; however, a careful analysis reveals immediate difficulties.

When the turbulence level is reasonably high, Taylor (1936a) successfully interpreted the transition phenomena in terms of the disturbances inside the boundary layer induced by the turbulence in the free stream. A relation connecting the Reynolds number of transition with the intensity and scale of turbulence is derived, and it was found to be in agreement with experimental observations (see Dryden et al., 1937). Taylor's argument uses a Pohlhausen parameter, which is a proper parameter essentially when the scale of the disturbance is large compared with that of the thickness of the boundary layer. If disturbances of smaller length scales are to be considered, a more refined treatment would be desirable.

A third cause of early transition is roughness on the wall.† Thus, looking at the transition problem as a whole, instability of the laminar motion represents only one of its aspects. However, the instability theory often suggests the correct parameters to be used for characterizing transition. For example, the parameter characterizing the instability of the boundary layer over a curved surface is $R_\theta(K\theta)^{\frac{1}{2}}$ (where K is the curvature of the surface, θ is the momentum thickness of the boundary layer, and R_θ is the Reynolds number based on it), and this parameter has been found to be also the proper one for characterizing transition. Theoretically, instability begins when the parameter $R_\theta(K\theta)^{\frac{1}{2}}$ reaches the value of the order of unity (see §6.2). Experimentally Liepmann found that this parameter varied between 6 and 9 at transition depending on the level of turbulence. The combined effect of pressure gradient and surface curvature is shown in fig. 6.2. It is seen that pressure gradient has a negligible influence on transition over a concave surface.

6.2. Various factors influencing the stability of the boundary layer

(i) *Effect of heating and cooling the boundary.* In the case of air, the effect of surface temperature on the stability of the boundary

---

† For a survey of the effect of roughness on transition, see, for example, the articles by Dryden (1953) and by Gazley (1953). The latter also contains an account of other factors influencing stability and transition of the boundary layer.

layer has been discussed before. Cooling has a stabilizing effect. In the case of water, cooling *increases* the coefficient of viscosity, and is therefore expected to have an opposite effect. The boundary layer would become unstable at a *lower* Reynolds number. In fact, in the absence of a pressure gradient, we have

$$\frac{\partial}{\partial y}\left(\mu\,\frac{\partial u}{\partial y}\right)=0$$

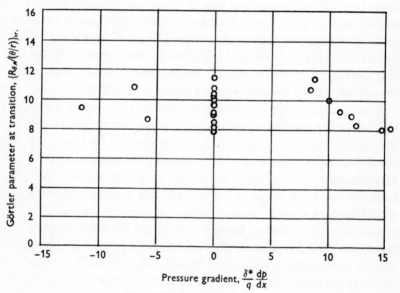

Fig. 6.2. Effect of the pressure gradient on transition on the concave side of a plate (after Liepmann, 1943).

at the wall. Consequently, the second derivative is

$$\frac{\partial^2 u}{\partial y^2}=-\frac{1}{\mu}\frac{\partial\mu}{\partial y}\frac{\partial u}{\partial y}\tag{6.2.1}$$

at the wall. The increase of temperature with increasing distance y makes $\partial\mu/\partial y$ negative. Hence, $\partial^2 u/\partial y^2$ starts out with a positive value but eventually becomes negative at large distances. The velocity profile must have a point of inflexion, suggesting increased instability. A full investigation of this phenomenon is not yet available in the literature.

(ii) *Effect of pressure gradient.* It has long been recognized that a decrease of pressure downstream favours the maintenance of a laminar boundary layer. On the other hand, an increase of pressure downstream will produce a point of inflexion in the velocity profile, making the flow unstable even in the inviscid limit. Fig. 6.3 *a* shows a typical neutral curve for such cases. Calculations of the effect of pressure gradient on the stability characteristics of the boundary layer were made by Schlichting and Ulrich (1942), by using a polynomical of degree six for the approximation to the velocity distribution. Their results were checked by Finston (Hahneman *et al.* 1948) using the approximation formulas in §5.4. Similar calculations (Pretsch, 1941 *b*) using the profiles computed by Hartree give results not significantly different. An extensive study of the incompressible laminar boundary layer on infinite wedges was made by Tetervin (1953). In the case of compressible fluids, calculations of the effect of pressure gradient were made by Lees (1950), Weil (1951) and Laurmann (1951). Complete stabilization of two-dimensional disturbances was found for a range of low supersonic Mach numbers (about 1·3 to 2·4) when there is a sufficiently high favourable pressure gradient. Fig. 6.3*b* shows the effect of pressure gradient on boundary-layer stability and transition. The transition data is for incompressible flow (Liepmann, 1945). The stability curves are from Hahneman *et al.* (1948) for the incompressible case and from Weil (1951) for the compressible case.

Low (1954) considered the combined effects of pressure gradient and cooling of the boundary on the stabilization of the boundary layer in the supersonic case. It is concluded that the effect of pressure gradient is usually very pronounced.

(iii) *Effect of suction and injection.* If the amount sucked away or injected into the flow from the boundary is not large, the boundary layer remains an approximately parallel flow, but has a changed profile. Suction makes the flow more stable, while injection makes it less stable. Calculations of the effect of suction, distributed in various ways along the boundary, were made by a number of people, for example Schlichting and Ulrich (1942), Bussmann and Münz (1942), Ulrich (1944) and Wuest (1953).† Tetervin and Levine

† A review of these earlier German works may be found in the report of Chiarulli and Freeman (1948).

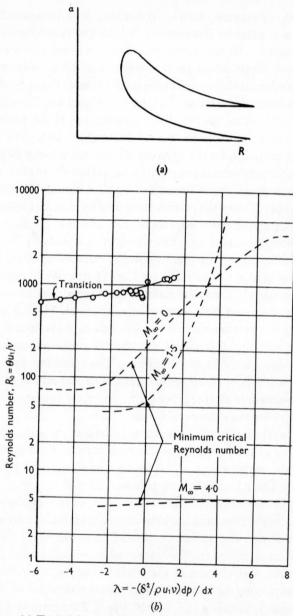

Fig. 6.3. (a) Typical form of the neutral curve for boundary layer under the influence of an adverse pressure gradient; first branch has an asymptote $\alpha = \alpha_s \neq 0$. (b) Effect of pressure gradient on boundary-layer stability and transition (after Gazley, 1953).

(1952) made a systematic investigation of the effects of changes in the boundary-layer thickness in regions of pressure gradient and flow through the surface. It is interesting to note that the effect of

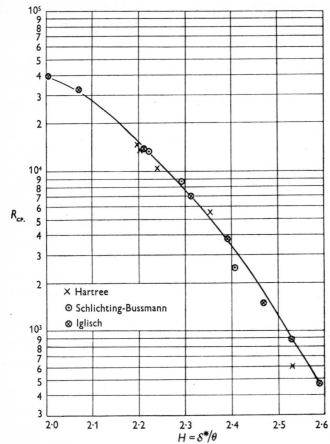

Fig. 6.4. Effect of pressure gradient and surface suction expressed in terms of the ratio of displacement thickness to momentum thickness.

suction may be easily correlated through the use of the form parameter

$$H = \delta^*/\theta. \tag{6.2.2}$$

Fig. 6.4† is a plot of the minimum critical Reynolds number versus H for the various profiles. The profiles calculated by Iglisch (1944)‡ are based on uniform suction over a flat plate; those by Schlichting

† From Chiarulli and Freeman (1948).
‡ Translated as *N.A.C.A. Tech. Memo.* no. 1205 (1949).

and Bussmann (1943) are for suction inversely proportional to the distance from the leading edge. Values of the critical Reynolds number for the Falkner–Skan profiles, as calculated by Hartree, are also included for comparison. They all lie approximately on the same curve.

In one particular case,[†] the velocity profile becomes

$$\bar{u} = 1 - e^{-y/\delta^*}, \tag{6.2.3}$$

and the solution of the inviscid equation can be obtained in terms of a hypergeometric function of the variable $z = e^{-y/\delta^*}$. By using this method, a detailed calculation was made by Freeman (see Chiarulli and Freeman, 1948) who obtained a minimum critical Reynolds number of 3.9×10^4. In this case, estimates based on Lin's approximation formula give the value 4.0×10^4.

(iv) *Effect of curvature of the boundary.* At first sight, it might be thought that the principal effect of the curvature of the boundary would be the modification of the pressure distribution. However, this is true only if the surface is *convex*. If the surface is *concave*, the dominant type of instability is similar to that found by Taylor (1923) between rotating cylinders and that found by Dean (1928) in a curved channel. Such a disturbance was first calculated by Görtler (1940b, 1941).

Indeed, if the disturbance is assumed to be of the type considered in Chapter 2, we obtain a characteristic-value problem very much the same as that considered there. We have to solve the differential equations

$$\left. \begin{aligned} \left(\frac{d^2}{dy^2} - \alpha^2 - \sigma R\right)\left(\frac{d^2}{dy^2} - \alpha^2\right)\hat{v} &= -2KR\bar{u}\alpha^2\hat{u}, \\ \left(\frac{d^2}{dy^2} - \alpha^2 - \sigma R\right)\hat{u} &= R\bar{u}'\hat{v}; \end{aligned} \right\} \tag{6.2.4}$$

subject to the boundary conditions

$$\left. \begin{aligned} \hat{u} = \hat{v} = \frac{d\hat{u}}{dy} = 0 \quad &\text{at the wall } y = 0, \\ \hat{u}, \hat{v} \text{ bounded at infinity.} & \end{aligned} \right\} \tag{6.2.5}$$

Here, $\bar{u}(y)$ denotes the dimensionless velocity distribution of the basic flow with respect to the dimensionless distance y, and R is the Reynolds number based on the free stream $\bar{u}_1$, and the thickness

[†] See H. Schlichting, *Luftfahrtf*, **19** (1942), p. 180.

δ of the boundary layer. The disturbance is periodic in a direction perpendicular to the flow plane with components having amplitudes $\hat{u}(y)$ and $\hat{v}(y)$, wavelength $2\pi\delta/\alpha$ and an exponential time factor of the form $\exp(\sigma t \bar{u}_1/\delta)$. The curvature of the boundary is K, positive if the surface is concave.

This characteristic-value problem was solved by Görtler in terms of the corresponding problem for integral equations. Only the case $\sigma = 0$ was treated. It is found that instability occurs when

$$R_\theta(K\theta)^{\frac{1}{2}} > 0.83. \tag{6.2.6}$$

Meksyn used an asymptotic method, considering α as a large parameter. He did not find instability until the above parameter reaches the value 3.65. Calculations made by Di Prima (1955), based on Galerkin's method, tend to confirm Görtler's original results.

Although these detailed calculations reveal most of the important characteristics of the lowest mode, there is as yet little information on the higher modes. In order to gain some insight into this problem, an inviscid investigation was suggested. If the viscous terms are neglected, we arrive at the equation

$$\frac{d^2\hat{v}}{dy^2} - \alpha^2\left(1 - \frac{2K}{\sigma^2}\overline{uu'}\right)\hat{v} = 0. \tag{6.2.7}$$

The boundary conditions are $\hat{v}(0) = 0$ and $\hat{v}(y)$ remains bounded at infinity. In fact, the equation (6.2.7) shows immediately the difference between positive and negative curvature. If exponentially growing solutions are to exist, $\sigma^2 > 0$. Now, the oscillation theorem† shows that the condition $2K\overline{uu'}/\sigma^2 > 1$ must be satisfied for some value of y if the characteristic-value problem of (6.2.7) has a solution. Since $\bar{u}' > 0$, this implies $K > 0$, that is, the surface must be concave. Furthermore, σ^2 is proportional to K for this mode of secondary motion, indicating that instability increases with surface curvature.

For special velocity profiles, the solution of (6.2.7) can be expressed in terms of well-known transcendental functions. Thus, if (6.2.3) holds, the solution is expressible in terms of Whittaker's function in the argument $z = e^{-y/\delta^*}$. If the velocity distribution is approximated by two straight lines, the solution can be expressed in terms of Hankel's function. D'Arcy‡ computed the first and

† See footnote, p. 51.   ‡ Master's thesis, M.I.T. (unpublished).

the second modes of the secondary flow by the latter method. The first mode shows a pattern very close to that obtained by Görtler. The second mode shows two cells.

6.3. The entry region in pipes and channels

As mentioned in Chapter 1, no theoretical indication of instability has ever been found for the fully developed parabolic profile in the case of the circular pipe. On the other hand, immediately at the entry of the pipe, the flow is essentially of the type of the boundary layer near the surface, and is uniform in the central part. Thus instability of the flow may be expected to arise from this boundary layer, as the speed of the central part is indefinitely increased.

Reasoning of this type has often been used to explain the origin of turbulent flow in pipes and channels. Recent investigations show that it needs careful examination. Actually, in the case of the channel, instability of the fully developed parabolic profile has been found to occur at a lower channel Reynolds number than that for the entry region. The reason is as follows.

Suppose we treat the basic flow as nearly parallel at each section of the channel. Then, for a given fluid, there is a critical speed for each section which decreases as the boundary-layer thickness increases downstream. On the other hand, there is a critical speed for the fully developed parabolic profile far downstream. It cannot be decided *a priori* which section would have the smallest critical speed, or equivalently, the minimum critical Reynolds number based on the width of the channel. It is immediately clear, however, that the critical Reynolds number based on channel width becomes infinite as the entry is approached, since the boundary-layer thickness there becomes infinitesimal compared with the channel width and the critical Reynolds number is 420 based on the displacement thickness of the boundary layer. Thus, a detailed calculation is needed.

For such purposes, an estimation of the minimum critical Reynolds number is desired for the various sections. This can be done by using the formula (Lin, 1945)

$$R = 30 \frac{\bar{u}'_w}{c^3} \left\{ \frac{\bar{u}'_w}{c} \int_0^1 \bar{u}^2 \, dy \right\}^{\frac{1}{2}}, \qquad (6.3.1)$$

where the Reynolds number R is now defined in terms of the maximum speed at the centre of the channel and its half-width, $\bar{u}(y)$ is the velocity distribution, $\bar{u}'_w$ is the slope of the distribution curve at the wall, both in dimensionless form, and c is a dimensionless speed determined by

$$\dot{v}(c) = \pi \frac{\overline{uu''}}{\overline{u}'^2} = 0.58. \qquad (6.3.2)$$

This formula was derived by admitting the approximation (3.5.13) and assuming that the minimum critical Reynolds number occurs at the maximum of $\mathcal{F}_i(z)$, namely, $\mathcal{F}_i = 0.58$, $\mathcal{F}_r = 1.49$ and $z = 3.21$. The formula (6.3.1) then follows from (3.5.13) and the relation

$$z = (\alpha R \bar{u}'_c)^{\frac{1}{3}} c / \bar{u}'_w = 3.21$$

(which follows from (3.6.6) after some obvious approximations). The constant coefficient 30 is an approximation of $(3.21)^3 (1.49)^{\frac{1}{2}}$. The formula (6.3.1) gives a minimum critical value of 5500 in the case of the fully developed parabolic velocity distribution. This compares favourably with the value 5300 found from detailed calculations.

Calculations were made by E. Hahneman *et al.* (1948), using equation (6.3.1), to find the critical Reynolds number at different sections of the two-dimensional channel. She found that this number decreases monotonically from infinity at the entry to the final value 5500 for the fully developed parabolic profile. Thus, in this case, instability first develops far downstream as the speed of flow is increased.

On the other hand, in the case of the circular pipe, it is expected that the fully developed parabolic profile is stable. The sectional critical Reynolds number is therefore expected to have a minimum somewhere in the entry region. This is indeed found to be the case by Tatsumi (1952a), who obtained a minimum critical Reynolds number of the order of 10^5. This is two to three times as large as the highest Reynolds number obtained experimentally by Eckman and by Taylor without instability being observed.[†]

In connexion with these discussions, one should also mention the earlier work of Schlichting (1932b) in the case of plane Couette flow. Schlichting considered the instability not of the linear profile, but the profile during its development from rest. In this way, he found a finite critical Reynolds number of the order of 10^3.

[†] See Goldstein (1938, p. 321).

6.4. Mixing of two parallel streams

The mixing region of two parallel streams gives rise to a type of problem of instability of nearly parallel flows somewhat different from that treated above. Such flows have two distinguishing characteristics: first, the presence of a point of inflexion in the velocity profile, and second, the absence of a solid boundary. These characteristics are common to flows in jets and wakes. We shall, however, treat the problem of the mixing region as a representative case. For definiteness let us consider first the case of an incompressible fluid.

From the existence of a point of inflexion in the velocity profile, we may immediately conclude that the flow is unstable in the limiting case of vanishing viscosity, and that it would become unstable at relatively low Reynolds numbers in the actual case. It may also be anticipated that the effect of viscosity would enter our problem in a manner different from the case of the usual boundary layer, because of the absence of the wall. In all previous cases, there is a viscous layer at the wall, where the viscous solution $\phi_3(y)$ becomes important. Here, the oscillations must extend to infinity in both directions across the jet, and such a layer does not exist.

Mathematically, if we apply the Orr–Sommerfeld equation to study the stability problem, and look for four asymptotic solutions in the manner of Chapter 3, we find four valid solutions by the first method. However, the boundedness of the disturbances at infinity immediately excludes the two solutions of the type (3.4.9). This means that the effect of viscosity can only enter through the Reynolds number R appearing in the *higher* approximations of solutions of the type (3.4.5).

The characteristic-value problem is therefore solved by finding a solution of the form (3.4.5) which is bounded for $y \to \pm\infty$. As noted before, such solutions in general possess a logarithmic singularity at $y = y_c$ where $w = c$. The region of validity of such a solution is determined by the condition that the real part of

$$Q = \int_{y_c}^{y} \sqrt{\{i(\bar{u} - c)\}} \, \mathrm{d}y$$

should change monotonically along the path as y changes from $-\infty$ to $+\infty$.

Such calculations have been carried out by M. Lessen (1950), whose results are shown in fig. 6.5. Two characteristics of the result are noteworthy. First, the critical Reynolds number of instability is very low, around 20. Secondly, the whole neutral curve lies below the line $\alpha = \alpha_s$, where α_s is the wave-number for the neutral disturbance in the non-viscous limit. In the case of the boundary layer

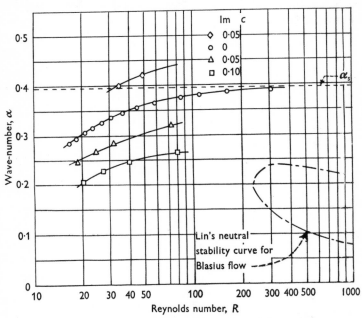

Fig. 6.5. Stability characteristics of the mixing region
(after Lessen, 1950).

under the influence of an adverse pressure gradient, it can be shown that for $\alpha = \alpha_s$, the flow is unstable at large but finite Reynolds numbers (Heisenberg's criterion—see Lin (1945) and cf. fig. 6.3 a). The contrast between this and the present case clearly demonstrates the effect of the presence or absence of the solid boundary.

In the case of a gas, the limitation to subsonic disturbances leads immediately to some criterion of stability with respect to two-dimensional disturbances. If the relative speed of the two streams exceeds the sum of the speeds of sound in these gas streams, it can be readily shown that two-dimensional subsonic disturbances are impossible (Lin, 1953). Three-dimensional disturbances should then be carefully considered. For some cases with instability, the amplification characteristics of the disturbances in the non-viscous limit have also been calculated.

The stability characteristics of a jet in a gas have been studied by Pai (1951). In the incompressible case, the stability of jets and wakes was investigated by Hollingdale (1940) and Savic (1941) in the inviscid limit.

CHAPTER 7

EXAMPLES OF STABILITY PROBLEMS OF INTEREST IN ASTROPHYSICS AND GEOPHYSICS

7.1. General remarks

As explained in the preface, it is impossible to give, in this volume, a comprehensive account of all the important problems on the stability of fluid motions. The previous discussions have been essentially limited to homogeneous fluids in the absence of external body forces. It seems desirable to treat a wider class of problems to show the influence of other factors on the stability of fluid motions. For this purpose, we discuss in this chapter some stability problems of interest in astrophysics and geophysics.

A treatment of specific problems in these fields is again beyond the scope of this book.[†] We shall merely present some simple examples to illustrate the influence of (i) Coriolis forces, (ii) gravitation and (iii) the electromagnetic field. The first two factors are important in meteorology; all three factors enter astrophysical problems.

In a series of papers, Chandrasekhar (see Bibliography) considered problems involving these effects. In particular, he considered (1954) the problem of thermal instability of a layer of fluid heated below and subjected simultaneously to Coriolis forces and an external magnetic field. In this case, all the three effects mentioned above are present. In the following, we shall only reproduce his discussion in the simpler cases; namely, the classical problem of thermal convection, and the modification of the problem by the influence of the magnetic field on an electrically conducting fluid. The influence of the Coriolis force will be exemplified by a simple meteorological problem treated by Kuo (1949, 1951) and by Foote and Lin (1950).

[†] For the treatment of one class of stability problems of astrophysical interest, see Lyttleton (1953). Stability problems of meteorological interest have been treated by Charney, Eady, Fjørtoft, Kuo, Queney, Solberg (see Bibliography), and others. In particular, see Kuo's (1953 a) discussion of the relation between the work of these authors and their conclusions. For problems involving interface between two fluids, see Taylor (1950), Lock (1954).

We shall find it possible to trace the general physical mechanism through which the above-mentioned factors influence the stability of fluid motion. When gravitational forces are important, the tendency for a lighter fluid to come on top of a heavier fluid will be a destabilizing influence. On the other hand, viscous forces will usually serve as a stabilizing influence against such a driving mechanism. The effect of the Coriolis force may often be traced through vorticity relations. In essence, we should consider the absolute vorticity of the fluid motion instead of its spinning relative to a rotating system. The magnetic field is in general stabilizing, as will be seen in §7.4. This is also demonstrated in the study of its influence on the two classical problems treated in Chapters 2 and 3, as was recently carried out respectively by Chandrasekhar (1953 b) and Stuart (1954). For a systematic discussion of such problems, the reader may consult Chandrasekhar's lecture (1954 d).

7.2. Stability of zonal winds in the atmosphere

One interesting application of the stability theory is the study of oscillations in the atmosphere. The scale of such motions is so large that the curvature of the earth should be taken into account. Still more important, there is the Coriolis force to be considered.

In the upper atmosphere, there is a strong westerly current, strongest at the tropopause. The stream lines exhibit a wavy pattern, similar to the oscillations in an ordinary jet. To examine such oscillations, one may consider an idealized model of a zonal current independent of altitude. It will be shown immediately that the amplitude of the oscillations in such a jet, after a Mercator projection, satisfies an equation very similar to that in a corresponding plane problem. It is especially noteworthy that the stability of the motion, like that of a two-dimensional parallel flow, depends also on the *gradient of vorticity*, although there are two important differences in its analytical expression. First, over a spherical earth, the vorticity of the motion depends on the velocity components of the motion in a somewhat more involved manner. Secondly, the rotation of the earth must be taken into account. Such results give further confidence to the physical mechanism of instability described in terms of vortex motions in Chapter 4.

Let us take an orthogonal coordinate system (ϕ, σ, z) over the surface of the earth, where ϕ is the longitude, σ is the distance from the equator along the meridian, positive towards the north pole, and z is the distance perpendicular to the surface. Consider the two-dimensional motion of a thin layer of fluid over the earth. Let u and v be the linear velocity components *relative* to the earth along the directions of increasing ϕ and σ, and let ζ be the component of the absolute vorticity in the direction of the z-axis. Then the vorticity equation is

$$\frac{\partial \zeta}{\partial t} + \frac{u}{r} \frac{\partial \zeta}{\partial \phi} + v \frac{\partial \zeta}{\partial \sigma} = 0, \qquad (7.2.1)$$

where r is the distance from the axis of rotation, and

$$\zeta = \zeta_n + \frac{1}{r} \left\{ \frac{\partial v}{\partial \phi} - \frac{\partial}{\partial \sigma}(ru) \right\}, \qquad (7.2.2)$$

where $\frac{1}{2}\zeta_n$ is the component of angular velocity, normal to the surface, of the spinning of the earth. The equation of continuity is

$$\frac{\partial u}{\partial \phi} + \frac{\partial}{\partial \sigma}(rv) = 0. \qquad (7.2.3)$$

Let us consider a motion slightly disturbed from a pure zonal motion

$$u = \bar{u}(\sigma) + u', \quad v = v'. \qquad (7.2.4)$$

The perturbations u', v' and ζ' then satisfy the linearized equations

$$\left. \begin{aligned} \frac{\partial u'}{\partial \phi} + \frac{\partial}{\partial \sigma}(rv') &= 0, \\ \frac{\partial \zeta'}{\partial t} + \frac{\bar{u}}{r} \frac{\partial \zeta'}{\partial \phi} + v \frac{d\bar{\zeta}}{d\sigma} &= 0, \end{aligned} \right\} \qquad (7.2.5)$$

with

$$\left. \begin{aligned} \bar{\zeta} &= \zeta_n - \frac{1}{r} \frac{d}{d\sigma}(r\bar{u}), \\ \zeta' &= \frac{1}{r} \left\{ \frac{\partial v'}{\partial \phi} - \frac{\partial}{\partial \sigma}(ru') \right\}. \end{aligned} \right\} \qquad (7.2.6)$$

It is now possible to set up an 'equivalent' plane motion by defining the following quantities:

$$\left. \begin{aligned} \mathbf{x} &= \phi, \quad \mathbf{y} = \int_0^\sigma \frac{d\sigma}{r}, \quad \bar{\mathbf{u}} = \frac{\bar{u}}{r}, \\ \mathbf{u}' &= ru', \quad \mathbf{v}' = rv', \quad \boldsymbol{\zeta}' = r^2 \zeta'; \end{aligned} \right\} \qquad (7.2.7)$$

then

$$\frac{\partial \mathbf{u}'}{\partial \mathbf{x}} + \frac{\partial \mathbf{v}'}{\partial \mathbf{y}} = 0,$$

$$\left.\frac{\partial \zeta'}{\partial t} + \bar{\mathbf{u}} \frac{\partial \zeta'}{\partial \mathbf{x}} + \mathbf{v}' \frac{d\bar{\zeta}}{d\mathbf{y}} = 0,\right\} \qquad (7.2.8)$$

$$\zeta' = \frac{\partial \mathbf{v}'}{\partial \mathbf{x}} - \frac{\partial \mathbf{u}'}{\partial \mathbf{y}}.$$

These are identical with the equations for a small disturbance in a two-dimensional flow. The boundary conditions are also similar to those in ordinary jets and wakes. The term $d\bar{\zeta}/d\mathbf{y}$ is, however, a more complicated expression than the simple form $-d^2\bar{\mathbf{u}}/d\mathbf{y}^2$, which would be the case if the motion were two-dimensional. But if we work with the gradient of vorticity,

$$G(y) = \frac{d\bar{\zeta}}{d\mathbf{y}}, \qquad (7.2.9)$$

the mathematical theory can be developed without essential modifications. In particular, the zonal current is unstable or stable according to whether this gradient vanishes or not.

Further discussions of the general theory were made by Foote and Lin (1950). The meteorological significance of these oscillations has been studied by Kuo (1949, 1951), who also made detailed calculations of the flow patterns of neutral oscillations and compared them with the observed patterns in the weather map.

7.3. Convective motion of a fluid heated from below

The manner of the onset of convection in an incompressible fluid by thermal instability has been the subject of investigations by Rayleigh (1916a), Jeffreys (1926), Low (1929), Pellew and Southwell (1940) and others. Recently, the effect of a magnetic field on such phenomena, when the fluid is conducting, has been treated independently by Thompson (1949, 1951) and Chandrasekhar (1952a). In this section, we shall treat the original problem of Rayleigh; in the next section, we shall consider the case with the magnetic field. It will be seen that the magnetic field may inhibit the convective motion in such a manner that the first instability will be associated with small oscillations with exponentially increasing amplitude.

Consider, for definiteness, a thin layer of liquid between two horizontal plates at $x_3 = 0$ and $x_3 = d$, where x_3 is the vertical distance. In rectangular coordinates, the equations of motion are

$$\rho_* \frac{Du_i}{D\tau} = \rho_* X_i - \frac{\partial \Pi}{\partial x_i} + \rho_* \nu_* \Delta u_i. \tag{7.3.1}$$

In this problem, the external forces are

$$(X_1, X_2, X_3) = (0, 0, -g) \tag{7.3.2}$$

per unit mass. The equation of continuity is

$$\frac{D\rho_*}{D\tau} + \rho_* \frac{\partial u_i}{\partial x_i} = 0, \tag{7.3.3}$$

and the equation of heat conduction is

$$\frac{D\Theta}{D\tau} = \kappa_* \Delta\Theta, \tag{7.3.4}$$

where κ_* is the thermometric conductivity. The equation of state for the fluid is

$$\rho_* = \rho_0 \{1 - \alpha(\Theta - \Theta_0)\}, \tag{7.3.5}$$

where α is the coefficient of expansion, and ρ_0 is the density of the fluid at the reference temperature Θ_0.

In the steady state, $u_i = 0$, and

$$\left.\begin{aligned}
\Theta &= \overline{\Theta} = \Theta_0 + \beta x_3, \\
\rho_* &= \overline{\rho}_* = \rho_0(1 - \alpha\beta x_3), \\
\frac{\partial \Pi}{\partial x_3} &= \frac{\partial \overline{\Pi}}{\partial x_3} = -g\rho_0(1 - \alpha\beta x_3),
\end{aligned}\right\} \tag{7.3.6}$$

where β is the temperature gradient,

$$\beta = (\Theta_1 - \Theta_0)/d, \tag{7.3.7}$$

and Θ_0 and Θ_1 are respectively the temperatures at the lower and the upper plates.

For a small perturbation, u_i are small. If we write

$$\left.\begin{aligned}
\Theta &= \overline{\Theta} + \Theta', \\
\Pi &= \overline{\Pi} + \Pi',
\end{aligned}\right\} \tag{7.3.8}$$

and neglect second-order terms in the disturbances, we find that (7.3.1), (7.3.3) and (7.3.4) reduce to

$$\frac{\partial u_i}{\partial \tau} = (0, 0, g\alpha\Theta') - \frac{1}{\rho_0} \frac{\partial \Pi'}{\partial x_i} + \nu_* \Delta u_i, \tag{7.3.9}$$

$$\frac{\partial u_i}{\partial x_i} = 0, \tag{7.3.10}$$

and
$$\left(\frac{\partial}{\partial \tau} - \kappa_* \Delta\right) \Theta' = -\beta u_3. \qquad (7.3.11)$$

By eliminating u_1', u_2', Π' from (7.3.9) and (7.3.10), we find that

$$\left(\frac{\partial}{\partial \tau} - \nu_* \Delta\right) \Delta u_3 = \gamma \Delta_1 \Theta', \quad \gamma = g\alpha, \qquad (7.3.12)$$

where $\Delta_1 = \dfrac{\partial^2}{\partial x_1^2} + \dfrac{\partial^2}{\partial x_2^2}$. This and (7.3.11) are the two final equations for Θ' and u_3, from which either one of the variables can be eliminated conveniently.

The boundary conditions at the fixed plates are

$$u_i = 0 \quad \text{and} \quad \Theta' = 0 \quad \text{at} \quad x_3 = 0, d, \qquad (7.3.13)$$

if the temperatures of the plates are fixed. It can be shown that the conditions $u_1 = u_2 = 0$ can be satisfied if

$$\frac{\partial u_3}{\partial x_3} = 0 \quad \text{at} \quad x_3 = 0, d. \qquad (7.3.14)$$

Other boundary conditions are of interest. For example, at a free surface, the pressure must remain undisturbed. We shall use these conditions when the occasion arises.

We try solutions of the form

$$\left.\begin{aligned}
&u_3 = (\kappa_*/d) f(x, y) w(z) e^{\sigma t}, \\
&\Theta' = (\Theta_1 - \Theta_0) f(x, y) \theta(z) e^{\sigma t}, \\
&\sigma = \sigma_* d^2/\kappa_*, \quad \sigma t = \sigma_* \tau, \quad (x, y, z) = \left(\frac{x_1}{d}, \frac{x_2}{d}, \frac{x_3}{d}\right).
\end{aligned}\right\} \qquad (7.3.15)$$

Then, we find that
$$\left.\begin{aligned}
f_{xx} + f_{yy} + a^2 f = 0, \\
[\sigma - (D^2 - a^2)]\theta = -w, \quad D = \frac{\partial}{\partial z}, \\
[\sigma Pr^{-1} - (D^2 - a^2)](D^2 - a^2)w = Ra^2\theta, \\
R = g\alpha(-\beta) d^4/\kappa_* \nu_*,
\end{aligned}\right\} \qquad (7.3.16)$$

where a^2 is a (dimensionless) constant arising from separation of variables. The boundary conditions are

$$w(z) = w'(z) = 0, \quad \theta(z) = 0 \quad \text{at} \quad z = 0, 1. \qquad (7.3.17)$$

These equations can be easily seen to be essentially the same as (2.2.3) and (2.2.4) if ω is constant in the first equation of (2.2.3).

Thus, there is an equivalence between the problem of convection and the secondary motion between rotating cylinders. This equivalence was suggested by Taylor and Low and demonstrated mathematically by Jeffreys (1928).

If we now assume, as in the case of rotating cylinders, that the threshold of instability is marked by $\sigma = 0$, we find, by analogous calculations, that this threshold is given by the Rayleigh number

$$R = \frac{g\alpha(-\beta)d^4}{\kappa_* \nu_*} = 1708, \qquad (7.3.18)$$

which occurs for $a = 3 \cdot 13$. The first equation of (7.3.16) may then be solved for the pattern of the motion. It is clear that such a pattern can be obtained by the superposition of solutions of the type

$$f(x,y) = \cos\frac{n_1 \pi x_1}{L_1} \cos\frac{n_2 \pi x_2}{L_2},$$

provided

$$\pi^2\left\{\left(\frac{n_1}{L_1}\right)^2 + \left(\frac{n_2}{L_2}\right)^2\right\} = \frac{a^2}{d^2}.$$

Experiments by Bénard (1901) show that the pattern is usually of the hexagonal shape, and Christopherson[†] (1940) pointed out that the appropriate solution for such a problem is

$$f(x,y) = f_0\left\{\cos\frac{2n\pi}{3L}(\sqrt{3}\,x_1 + x_2)\right.$$
$$\left. + \cos\frac{2n\pi}{3L}(\sqrt{3}\,x_1 - x_2) + \cos\frac{4n\pi x_2}{3L}\right\}, \quad (7.3.19)$$

where L is the length of a side, and is given by

$$\frac{aL}{d} = \frac{4n\pi}{3}. \qquad (7.3.20)$$

Pellew and Southwell were, however, able to show that the threshold of instability *must* be marked by $\sigma = 0$. In essence, their proof is as follows. If we multiply the second equation of (7.3.16) by θ^*, and integrate between $z = 0$ and $z = 1$, we find that

$$\sigma\int_0^1 |\theta|^2\,dz + \int_0^1 \{|D\theta|^2 + a^2 |\theta|^2\}\,dz = -\int_0^1 w\theta^*\,dz. \qquad (7.3.21)$$

[†] Christopherson, D. G., 'Note on the vibration of membranes', *Quart. J. Math.* **11**, 63–5.

Similarly, if we multiply the third equation of (7.3.16) by w^* and integrate, we obtain

$$\frac{\sigma}{Pr}\int_0^1 \{|\,Dw\,|^2 + a^2|\,w\,|^2\}\,dz + \int_0^1 \{|\,D^2w\,|^2 + 2a^2|\,Dw\,|^2 + a^4|\,w\,|^2\}dz$$
$$= -Ra^2\int_0^1 w^*\theta\,dz. \quad (7.3.22)$$

From the first equation of (7.3.16) it can be seen that $a^2 > 0$. Hence the integrals

$$I_0 = \int_0^1 |\,\theta\,|^2\,dz, \quad I_1 = \int_0^1 \{|\,D\theta\,|^2 + a^2|\,\theta\,|^2\}\,dz,$$

$$J_1 = \int_0^1 \{|\,Dw\,|^2 + a^2|\,w\,|^2\}\,dz,$$

$$J_2 = \int_0^1 \{|\,D^2w\,|^2 + 2a^2|\,Dw\,|^2 + a^4|\,w\,|^2\}dz$$

are all positive. The right-hand sides of (7.3.21) and (7.3.22) are complex conjugates except for some real factors. Thus we find

$$-Ra^2(\sigma^* I_0 + I_1) + (\sigma\frac{J_1}{Pr} + J_2) = 0,$$

or
$$\sigma_r(-Ra^2 I_0 + \frac{J_1}{Pr}) + (-RI_1 + J_2) = 0, \\ \sigma_i(Ra^2 I_0 + \frac{J_1}{Pr}) = 0. \quad (7.3.23)$$

If $\sigma_i \neq 0$, then
$$\frac{J_1}{Pr} = -Ra^2 I_0,$$

and $R < 0$. The first equation then shows that $\sigma_r < 0$, i.e. the motion must be stable. Actually, we see that the condition

$$R < 0$$

means that the temperature gradient is positive, that is, that the density of the fluid *decreases* upwards. Physically, this is clearly a stable case. On the other hand, in the unstable case, all the characteristic roots are real, confirming the principle of exchange of stabilities.

7.4. Convective motion in the presence of a magnetic field

We shall now reconsider the above problem for an electrically conducting fluid in the presence of a magnetic field, following essentially Chandrasekhar (1952a).

The equations of motion, of Maxwell, and of heat conduction are†

$$\rho_* \frac{\partial u_i}{\partial \tau} - \mu_e \epsilon_{imn} j_m H_n = -\frac{\partial \Pi}{\partial x_i} + \rho_* \nu_* \Delta u_i - \rho_* \frac{\partial V}{\partial x_i}, \quad (7.4.1)$$

$$\left. \begin{array}{c} \epsilon_{mik} \dfrac{\partial H_k}{\partial x_i} = 4\pi j_m, \quad \epsilon_{mik} \dfrac{\partial E_k}{\partial x_i} = -\mu_e \dfrac{\partial H_m}{\partial \tau}, \\[2mm] \dfrac{\partial H_k}{\partial x_k} = 0, \quad j_m = \sigma_e(E_m + \mu_e \epsilon_{mik} u_i H_k), \end{array} \right\} \quad (7.4.2)$$

and
$$\frac{D\Theta}{D\tau} = \kappa_* \Delta\Theta, \quad (7.4.3)$$

where ρ_* denotes the density, Π the pressure, Θ the temperature, V the gravitational potential, E_i the intensity of the electric field, H_i the intensity of the magnetic field, j_m the current density, μ_e the magnetic permeability, and ν_*, κ_* and σ_e are the coefficients of kinematic viscosity, thermometric conductivity, and electric conductivity respectively. The electromagnetic system of units is used.

In the above equations, the displacement current is ignored. This is well known to be a permissible approximation in the problems of magneto-hydrodynamics. It is then possible to eliminate the current density j_m from (7.4.1) by means of the first equation of (7.4.2). By making use of the solenoidal property of H_m, we can then reduce (7.4.1) into the form

$$\rho_* \frac{Du_i}{D\tau} = -\frac{\partial \Pi}{\partial x_i} + \rho_* \nu_* \Delta u_i - \rho_* \frac{\partial V}{\partial x_i} + \frac{\partial S_{ij}}{\partial x_j}, \quad (7.4.4)$$

where S_{ij} is Maxwell's magnetic stress,

$$S_{ij} = \frac{\mu_e}{4\pi}(H_i H_j - \tfrac{1}{2}H^2 \delta_{ij}). \quad (7.4.5)$$

If we now eliminate E_m and j_m from the Maxwell equations (7.4.2), we find

$$\frac{DH_i}{D\tau} = H_j \frac{\partial u_i}{\partial x_j} + \eta_e \Delta H_i, \quad \eta_e = \frac{1}{4\pi \mu_e \sigma_e}. \quad (7.4.6)$$

Thus, the magnetic field behaves very much like the vorticity field.‡

† Displacement current neglected. ϵ_{imn} is the alternating symbol; it is equal to $+1$ if (i, m, n) has the cyclic order $(1, 2, 3)$, -1 if (i, m, n) has the cyclic order $(2, 1, 3)$, and equal to zero otherwise.
‡ Cf. G. K. Batchelor, *Proc. Roy. Soc.* A, **201**, 405 (1950).

If we now apply the basic equations (7.4.3), (7.4.4) and (7.4.6) to the study of the problem of the last section with a magnetic field in the vertical direction, we find the following equations for small disturbances:

$$\left.\begin{aligned}
\frac{\partial u_3}{\partial \tau} &= \frac{\mu_e H}{4\pi\rho_0}\frac{\partial h}{\partial x_3} + \gamma\Theta' + \nu_*\Delta u_3 - \frac{\partial \varpi}{\partial x_3}, \\
\frac{\partial \Theta'}{\partial \tau} &= -\beta u_3 + \kappa_*\Delta\Theta', \\
\frac{\partial h}{\partial \tau} &= H\frac{\partial u_3}{\partial x_3} + \eta_e\Delta h, \\
\Delta\varpi &= \gamma\frac{\partial \Theta'}{\partial x_3},
\end{aligned}\right\} \qquad (7.4.7)$$

where u_3, Θ', h are the small disturbances of the vertical velocity, the temperature, and the magnetic field, and ϖ stands for

$$\varpi = \frac{\Pi}{\rho_0} + \frac{\mu_e H^2}{8\pi\rho_0} + gx_3 - \tfrac{1}{2}\beta\gamma x_3^2. \qquad (7.4.8)$$

The other symbols have the same meaning as in §7.3. The boundary conditions are

$$\Theta' = u_3 = 0, \quad \frac{\partial u_3}{\partial x_3} = 0 \quad \text{for} \quad x_3 = 0, d, \qquad (7.4.9)$$

for rigid surfaces. If the surfaces are free, the last condition should be replaced by

$$\frac{\partial^2 u_3}{\partial x_3^2} = 0. \qquad (7.4.10)$$

In the previous case, Pellew and Southwell have proved that the principle of exchange of stabilities holds. In the present case, the method used by Pellew and Southwell is not sufficiently strong to establish such a principle. In fact, Chandrasekhar found a condition for the principle *not* to be valid. For a special case, the principle *is* valid if

$$\eta_e > \kappa_*. \qquad (7.4.11)$$

This is true under terrestrial conditions; but under astrophysical conditions $\eta_e \ll \kappa_*$, and the principle fails. Instability of the oscillatory type occurs. Chandrasekhar gave detailed discussions for the astrophysical conditions, for which $\kappa_* \gg \eta_e \gg \nu_*$. He concluded that the inhibition of the onset of *instability* by a magnetic field is *not* very pronounced. On the other hand, in all practical cases, the instability may be expected to develop in the form of oscillations of increasing amplitude, the question whether there will be true convection in these cases becomes uncertain.

If the principle of exchange of instabilities is accepted, Chandrasekhar has shown that the solution at marginal stability can again be obtained by a variational principle. In fact, if we write (cf. (7.3.15)),

$$u_3 = (\kappa_*/d)f(x,y)w(z), \quad \Theta' = (\Theta_1 - \Theta_0)f(x,y)\theta(z), \quad (7.4.12)$$

we obtain, analogous to (7.3.16), with $\sigma = 0$,

$$[(D^2 - a^2)^2 - QD^2]w = -Ra^2\theta, \quad (7.4.13)$$

and
$$(D^2 - a^2)\theta = w, \quad (7.4.14)$$

where
$$Q = \frac{\mu_e^2 H^2 \sigma_e}{\rho_0 \nu_*}d^2 \quad \text{and} \quad R = -\frac{\beta\gamma}{\kappa_*\nu_*}d^4. \quad (7.4.15)$$

The boundary conditions are

$$\left.\begin{array}{ll}\theta = w = 0 & \text{for } z = 0, 1, \\ Dw = 0 & \text{on rigid surface,} \\ D^2w = 0 & \text{on free surface.}\end{array}\right\} \quad (7.4.16)$$

If we now write

$$\left.\begin{array}{l}\mathscr{R} = I_1/a^2 I_2, \\ I_1 = \displaystyle\int_0^1 \{(DF)^2 + a^2 F^2\}\,dz, \\ I_2 = \displaystyle\int_0^1 \{[(D^2 - a^2)w]^2 + Q(Dw)^2\}\,dz,\end{array}\right\} \quad (7.4.17)$$

where
$$F = [(D^2 - a^2)^2 - QD^2]w, \quad (7.4.18)$$

then
$$\delta\mathscr{R} = 0 \quad (7.4.19)$$

for arbitrary variations δw satisfying (7.4.16) would lead to the equations (7.4.13) and (7.4.14). This is also equivalent to the variational problem

$$\delta I_1 = 0 \quad \text{with subsidiary condition } I_2 = \text{constant.} \quad (7.4.20)$$

This latter form is formally derived by regarding θ as defined in terms of w by (7.4.13), multiplying (7.4.14) by $\delta\theta$ and integrating by parts.

Chandrasekhar worked out the dependence of R on Q by the Rayleigh method for the cases: (i) when both bounding surfaces are free, (ii) when both are rigid, and (iii) when one bounding surface is free and the other is rigid. The critical value R_c, that is, the minimum value of R with respect to a is calculated in each case for various values of Q. For Q of the order of 10^4, this critical value is of the order of a hundred times that at $Q = 0$.

CHAPTER 8

MATHEMATICAL THEORY FOR THE STABILITY OF PARALLEL FLOWS

8.1. Asymptotic solutions for large Reynolds numbers

In this chapter, a discussion will be given of the basic mathematical theory underlying the analysis of the stability of parallel flows. In order to clarify the main difficulties and to explain their solution without unnecessary complications, the discussion will be limited to the incompressible case. We begin by recapitulating the boundary-value problem formulated in Chapter 1 for the case of flow through a channel, with emphasis on the mathematical aspects.

The amplitude function $\phi(y)$ for the small disturbances satisfies the Orr–Sommerfeld equation

$$\phi^{\mathrm{iv}} - 2\alpha^2\phi'' + \alpha^4\phi = i\alpha R\{(w-c)(\phi'' - \alpha^2\phi) - w''\phi\}, \quad (8.1.1)$$

where $w(y)$ is a given function of y, α and R are real parameters, and c is a complex parameter. Physically speaking, the function $w(y)$ is the velocity distribution for the basic parallel flow. It is therefore defined only for real values of y in an interval (y_1, y_2), if the flow is between the planes $y = y_1$ and $y = y_2$. Furthermore, the exact solution of the Navier–Stokes equations shows that $w(y)$ can only be a quadratic function of y. For our present purposes, we shall, however, consider $w(y)$ to be a fairly general analytic function of the complex variable y, which is obtained by the analytic continuation of the function given by the physical velocity distribution. Neither shall we limit ourselves to a quadratic function of y, so that the theory *could* be applied to other nearly parallel flows.†

Certain boundary conditions are to be satisfied at the end-points y_1 and y_2. If both of these points represent solid boundaries, then

$$\left.\begin{aligned} \phi(y_1) &= \phi(y_2) = 0, \\ \phi'(y_1) &= \phi'(y_2) = 0. \end{aligned}\right\} \quad (8.1.2)$$

† Here we take the point of view of attacking the mathematical problem obtained by treating such flows *as if* they were parallel. The justification of such a process will have to be settled separately for each class of physical problems.

If an end-point goes to infinity, the corresponding condition is the boundedness of the solution. For definiteness, we shall usually refer to the boundary conditions (8.1.2). The necessary modifications under other circumstances can be easily made.

The coefficients in (8.1.1) are analytic functions of y and depend analytically on the parameters α, R and c. There is thus a fundamental system of solutions having these same analytical properties. Solutions satisfying the condition (8.1.2) exist only when the parameters α, R and c are connected by the *secular equation*,

$$\mathbf{F}(\alpha, R, c) = 0. \tag{8.1.3}$$

We usually regard c as the parameter whose characteristic values are sought for given values of α and R. The characteristic values of c are in general complex, $c = c_r + ic_r$. Our chief interest is to determine the sign of its imaginary part, c_i ($c_i > 0$, unstable; $c_i < 0$, stable; $c_i = 0$, neutral).

Experiments and experience suggest that instability can be found only for large values of αR; and one is therefore led to consider the appropriate asymptotic solutions of (8.1.1) in such cases.

Two formal asymptotic methods are described in Chapter 3. In the first method, a fundamental system of four solutions is obtained in two groups. The first group of two solutions is of the form

$$\phi(y) = \phi^{(0)}(y) + (\alpha R)^{-1} \phi^{(1)}(y) + ..., \tag{8.1.4}$$

where the initial approximation $\phi^{(0)}(y)$ satisfies the inviscid equation (obtained by *neglecting* viscosity from (8.1.1))

$$(w - c)(\phi'' - \alpha^2 \phi) - w'' \phi = 0, \tag{8.1.5}$$

and the higher approximations are determined by differential equations obtained by formally substituting (8.1.4) into (8.1.1) and equating coefficients of powers of $(\alpha R)^{-1}$. The second group of two solutions is of the form

$$\phi(y) = e^{\pm (\alpha R)^{\frac{1}{2}} Q(y)} \{ f_0(y) + (\alpha R)^{-\frac{1}{2}} f_1(y) + ... \}, \tag{8.1.6}$$

where
$$Q(y) = \int_{y_c}^{y} \sqrt{\{i(w - c)\}} \, dy, \quad f_0(y) = (w - c)^{-\frac{5}{4}}.... \tag{8.1.7}$$

Here the higher approximations can be obtained from first-order differential equations, which are solvable by direct quadrature. These equations are obtained by formally substituting (8.1.7) into (8.1.1) and comparing coefficients of powers of $(\alpha R)^{\frac{1}{2}}$.

We observe, however, that this method gives solutions with a branch point at the critical point $y = y_c$. This is obvious in the two solutions (8.1.6). For the solutions (8.1.4), this is seen by a direct application of the method of Frobenius to the inviscid equation (8.1.7). By using this method, Tollmien (1929) found two solutions of the form

$$\left.\begin{aligned} \phi_1(y) &= (y - y_c) P(y - y_c), \\ \phi_2(y) &= 1 + \ldots + \frac{w_c''}{w_c'} \phi_1(y) \log(y - y_c), \end{aligned}\right\} \tag{8.1.8}$$

where $P(y - y_c)$ is a power series in $y - y_c$ beginning with a constant term, $w_c' = w'(y_c)$ and $w_c'' = w''(y_c)$. The solution $\phi_2(y)$ is seen to be multiple-valued unless $w''(y_c) = 0$.

The decision of the proper branch of the multiple-valued expressions is one of the main problems with solutions of this type.

In the second asymptotic method, the solutions are obtained in the form

$$\phi(y) = \chi^{(0)}(\eta) + \epsilon \chi^{(1)}(\eta) + \ldots, \tag{8.1.9}$$

where

$$\epsilon = (\alpha R)^{-\frac{1}{3}} \quad \text{and} \quad \eta = (y - y_c)/\epsilon. \tag{8.1.10}$$

Four solutions are obtained at once when (8.1.9) is substituted into (8.1.1) and coefficients of the various powers of ϵ are compared. These solutions are all regular, and are expressed in terms of the function $\zeta^{\frac{1}{2}} H_{\frac{1}{3}}^{(1),(2)}[\frac{2}{3}(i\zeta)^{\frac{3}{2}}]$, where $\zeta = (w_c')^{\frac{1}{3}} \eta$.

It is clear from their method of derivation that the first solution (8.1.4), (8.1.6) is intended to be asymptotic representations for *fixed y and αR becoming infinite*. The second method (8.1.9) is intended to be asymptotic representations for *fixed η and αR becoming infinite*. In terms of y, the latter implies $y \to y_c$ as $\alpha R \to \infty$. Thus, both methods of solution are limited in their application.

Improved solutions which are free from these difficulties have recently been given by Tollmien (1947) for the neutral case and for real values of y. A more complete theory has been given by Wasow (1953 b) dealing with the general complex case. However, unlike the two previous methods, neither one of the methods contains an algorism for calculating the higher approximations; only the leading terms of the asymptotic solutions are obtained. The details of these investigations will be presented in §8.8.

The inherent intricacy of the asymptotic behaviour of the solutions of (8.1.1) is perhaps the basic cause of the controversy in the subject. It also makes the task very difficult to obtain adequate and simple representations of the solutions. Even though the more complete theory is now available, current calculations are usually based on the simpler representations obtained by the first two methods. These are often found to give adequate numerical approximations if properly used.

Classification of characteristic values. The two methods of asymptotic solution suggest that one might divide the stability problem into the following two classes:

Class I: Characteristic values that do not approach, as $\alpha R \to \infty$, the flow speed at either one of the boundary points, and

Class II: Characteristic values that approach these special values.

In the first case, the first asymptotic method gives adequate solutions, since the boundary points are at finite distances from the critical point y_c, and consequently these asymptotic solutions may be used. All that remains is the determination of the proper branches.

In the limit $\alpha R \to \infty$, we may expect class I to have an inviscid limit with $c \neq w(y_1)$ or $w(y_2)$ (cf. §8.2). However, it is not obvious that this must be the case (cf. §8.4). We may therefore subdivide class I as follows:

Class IA: Characteristic values that approach those of a limiting inviscid problem, and

Class IB: Characteristic values that are not related to the inviscid problem.

C. S. Morawetz (1952) has shown, however, that class IB always represent stable solutions.

8.2. Instability theory for perfect fluids

In order to appreciate the difficulty encountered in a naïve attempt, let us now try to develop the theory of stability for perfect fluids. If viscous forces are absent, the basic equation is (8.1.5), which may also be written as

$$\phi'' - \alpha^2 \phi - \frac{w''}{w-c} \phi = 0. \tag{8.2.1}$$

The boundary conditions are

$$\phi(y_1) = \phi(y_2) = 0, \tag{8.2.2}$$

corresponding to the vanishing of the velocity of fluctuation normal to the boundary. The other two conditions in (8.1.2) relate to the tangential component and need not be satisfied in the non-viscous case. We have thus an adequate formulation of a theory in terms of the characteristic-value problem of a differential equation of the second order. Such a theory should apply if the fluid has no viscosity to begin with. Whether it gives a proper limiting theory for the viscous problem has to be examined very carefully.

We have noted before that the equation (8.1.5) has a critical point where $w(y) = c$. If this critical point y_c coincides with one of the end-points, the boundary condition $\phi = 0$ would exclude the singular solution in (8.1.8). This case should therefore be treated separately. Unless otherwise stated, it will be tacitly assumed in the following discussions that c is neither equal to $w(y_1)$ nor equal to $w(y_2)$.

It is natural to proceed with the investigation as follows: We try to find a solution of (8.1.5) which is regular in the interval (y_1, y_2) and which satisfies the boundary conditions $\phi(y_1) = \phi(y_2) = 0$. Clearly, such a regular solution does not exist if the critical point y_c lies in this interval, and $w''(y_c) \neq 0$. This points to an obvious difficulty in the neutral case. For the self-excited case $(c_i > 0)$ and the damped case $(c_i < 0)$, such difficulties do not seem to occur. In fact, equation (8.2.1) suggests immediately that damped and self-excited disturbances are complex conjugates, and that one need only examine the case of self-excited disturbances. Accordingly, the following discussions will be restricted to such cases $c_i \geqslant 0$. However, when we try to make deductions about the damped case, serious difficulties appear. The damped case will therefore be treated in detail in §§ 8.3–8.4.

We shall now develop certain general theorems regarding (i) self-excited disturbances, (ii) neutral disturbances, and (iii) the role of the point of inflexion in the velocity profile.

(i) *Self-excited disturbances.* We observe that, in this case, the critical point y_c does not occur in the real interval (y_1, y_2). If we multiply (8.2.1) by ϕ^*, the complex conjugate of ϕ, and subtract from the resultant equation its complex conjugate, we obtain

$$\frac{d}{dy}(\phi'\phi^* - \phi^{*\prime}\phi) = \frac{c - c^*}{|w - c|^2} w'' |\phi|^2. \qquad (8.2.3)$$

Clearly, both sides of this equation are purely imaginary. If we introduce the real quantity

$$W = \frac{i}{2}(\phi\phi^{*\prime} - \phi^*\phi'),$$ (8.2.4)

then (8.2.3) may be written as†

$$\frac{dW}{dy} = \frac{c_i w''}{|w-c|^2}|\phi|^2.$$ (8.2.5)

Since either of the boundary conditions $\phi = 0$ or $\phi' = 0$ implies $W = 0$, we see that dW/dy must change its sign in the interval (y_1, y_2). Hence, *if a self-excited disturbance is to exist, $w''(y)$ must vanish somewhere between y_1 and y_2; the velocity distribution must have a point of inflexion.* This is Rayleigh's theorem discussed in §4.3. The above derivation is somewhat different from Rayleigh's original proof; it has the added advantage of giving a formula for the Reynolds stress.

The observation at the beginning of the preceding paragraph has another immediate consequence: the function $f(y) = \phi(y)/(w-c)$ is regular in the interval (y_1, y_2). In terms of $f(y)$, equation (8.2.1) becomes

$$\frac{d}{dy}\{(w-c)f'\} - \alpha^2(w-c)f = 0.$$

If we multiply this equation by f^* and integrate between y_1 and y_2, we obtain

$$\int_{y_1}^{y_2}(w-c)^2\{|f'|^2 + \alpha^2|f|^2\}\,dy = 0,$$ (8.2.6)

after transforming the first term by partial integration. The imaginary part of (8.2.6) gives

$$c_i\int_{y_1}^{y_2}(w-c_r)\{|f'|^2 + \alpha^2|f|^2\}\,dy = 0,$$

which shows that *c_r must lie between the maximum and the minimum of $w(y)$ in the interval y_1 and y_2.*

† With this formula, we can obtain the equation for the distribution of the Reynolds stress $\tau = -\rho\overline{u'v'}$, which can easily be shown to be equal to $\frac{1}{2}\rho\alpha W e^{2\alpha c_i t}$. We have also the relation $\overline{v^2} = \frac{1}{2}\alpha^2|\phi|^2 e^{2\alpha c_i t}$, so that (8.2.4) becomes

$$d\tau/dy = \rho\overline{v^2}(c_i w''/|\alpha w - c|^2),$$

which is equation (4.3.5).

(ii) *Neutral disturbances.* If we let $c_i \to 0$ in (8.2.5) and (8.2.6), we arrive at results important for neutral disturbances. From (8.2.5) we obtain
$$W = \text{const.}, \qquad (8.2.7)$$
except possibly at the critical point y_c, which may now lie in the real interval (y_1, y_2). If it does (and the relation (8.2.6) shows it must, as we shall see towards the end of this section), W has a discontinuity at that point of magnitude†
$$[W] = W(c+0) - W(c-0) = \pi(w_c''/w_c') |\phi_c|^2. \qquad (8.2.8)$$
This is seen as follows: If we integrate (8.2.5) from $y_3 = y_c - \delta$ to $y_4 = y_c + \delta$ we have
$$W(y_c + \delta) - W(y_c - \delta) = \int_{w_3}^{w_4} \frac{w''}{w'} |\phi|^2 \frac{c_i\, dw}{(w - c_r)^2 + c_i^2}.$$
In the limit $c_i \to 0$, the right-hand side approaches $\pi(w_c''/w_c') |\phi_c|^2$, provided that $c_i > 0$ and $w_4 > w_3$, in accordance with a well-known relation in potential theory.‡ Remembering that $w_4 - w_3$ could be positive or negative, we put the result in the form (8.2.8) in terms of $W(c \pm 0)$.

Equation (8.2.8) shows that $w''(y)$ *must change its sign in the interval* (y_1, y_2) *if a neutral disturbance is to exist,*§ since the *total* change of W between these points must be zero. There are two possibilities: either $w'' = 0$ at all the points where $w = c$, or several of the jumps $[W]$ cancel out, since $W = \text{const.}$ except for such jumps. If the velocity distribution is monotone, the former possibility must prevail. In this case, equation (8.2.1) has regular coefficients.

We observe that equation (8.2.6) was derived solely on the assumption that $f(y) = \phi(y)/(w - c)$ is regular in the interval (y_1, y_2). It can therefore be applied to neutral disturbances either when c lies beyond the range $(w_{\min.}, w_{\max.})$ or when $\phi(y)$ vanishes at the same point y_c. When equation (8.2.6) does apply, it shows that *the only*

---

† This relation was obtained by Tollmien (1935 b) by using the explicit solutions (8.1.8).

‡ $\lim\limits_{y \to 0} \int_{\xi_1}^{\xi_2} f(\xi)\, d\xi\, y\{(x - \xi)^2 + y^2\}^{-1} = \pm \pi f(x)$ is the relation connecting the field strength with the strength of the distributed source on the line $y = 0$. The positive sign obtains if $\xi_2 > x > \xi_1$ and $y > 0$. The reversal of either one of these conditions reverses the sign of the limit.

§ The possibility $\phi_c = 0$ may be excluded by a repetition of the argument between y_1 and y_c, since $\phi_c = 0$ leads to $W_c = 0$ (cf. (8.2.4)).

possible non-trivial neutral solution is given by $\alpha = 0$, $f(y) = const$. The latter is a solution if the boundary conditions are properly satisfied. For example, when the velocity $w(y)$ vanishes at y_1 and y_2, a possible solution is $\phi(y) = w(y)$ corresponding to $c = 0$.

(iii) *Point of inflexion in the velocity profile.* Consider first the velocity distributions without a point of inflexion. We see that neither self-excited nor neutral disturbances are possible, except for the singular solution just discussed (which is not an oscillation, but represents a steady deviation). Damped disturbances would also be excluded *if* they were indeed complex conjugates of the self-excited disturbances. This is a rather paradoxical situation, and will be fully discussed in the next section.

Consider now velocity distributions with a point of inflexion. In many cases, the general nature of the velocity distribution allows the singular solution $\alpha = 0$, $f(y) = w(y) - c$. In such cases, the existence of the point of inflexion generally insures the existence of the neutral oscillation with $w_c'' = 0$; i.e. if we denote the conditions at the point of inflexion by the subscript s, we have a solution with $c = w_s$. To prove this, consider the characteristic-value problem of the differential equation

$$\phi'' + \lambda\phi + K(y)\,\phi = 0, \quad K(y) = -w''(y)/(w - w_s), \quad (8.2.9)$$

with the parameter λ. We impose the conditions $w(y) > 0$, $K(y) > 0$, which are often satisfied. The oscillation theorem† then guarantees the existence of negative characteristic values of λ, that is, real values for $\alpha = \sqrt{-\lambda}$. Also, the corresponding solution $\phi_s(y)$ is real.

In such cases, the neutral solution also has neighbouring self-excited solutions. This is shown by considering the dependence of c on $\lambda = -\alpha^2$ in the characteristic-value problem of (8.2.1). We have just shown that there is a solution $\phi_s(y)$ corresponding to the characteristic values $c = c_s$, $-\alpha^2 = \lambda_s$. Thus,

$$\phi_s'' + \lambda_s\phi_s - \frac{w''}{w - c_s}\phi_s = 0. \quad (8.2.10)$$

If we now multiply (8.2.1) by ϕ_s, (8.2.10) by ϕ and subtract, there results

$$\frac{d}{dy}(\phi_s\phi' - \phi_s'\phi) + (\lambda - \lambda_s)\,\phi\phi_s - \left(\frac{w''}{w - c} - \frac{w''}{w - c_s}\right)\phi\phi_s = 0. \quad (8.2.11)$$

† See footnote, p. 51.

Integrating between the limits y_1 and y_2, we obtain

$$(\lambda - \lambda_s) \int_{y_1}^{y_2} \phi \phi_s \, dy = (c - c_s) \int_{y_1}^{y_2} \frac{w''}{(w-c)(w-c_s)} \phi \phi_s \, dy.$$

We now consider the limit as $\lambda \to \lambda_s$, $c \to c_s$ and $\phi \to \phi_s$. We introduce again $K(y) = -w''(y)/(w - c_s)$, which is a positive function. Then

$$-\left(\frac{d\lambda}{dc}\right)_s \int_{y_1}^{y_2} \phi_s^2 \, dy = \lim_{c \to c_s} \int_{y_1}^{y_2} \frac{K(y)}{w-c} \phi_s^2 \, dy. \qquad (8.2.12)$$

In terms of its real and imaginary parts, the integral on the right-hand side is

$$\int_{y_1}^{y_2} \frac{K(y)}{w-c} \phi_s^2 \, dy = \int_{y_1}^{y_2} \frac{K(y)(w-c_r)}{(w-c_r)^2 + c_i^2} \phi_s^2 \, dy + i \int_{y_1}^{y_2} \frac{K(y) c_i}{(w-c_r)^2 + c_i^2} \phi_s^2 \, dy.$$

The limit of the real part becomes the principal value of the integral $\int_{y_1}^{y_2} K(y)(w - c_s)^{-1} \, dy$, the imaginary part tends to the limit $\pi K(y_c) \phi_s^2(y_s) > 0$, since $c_i \to 0$ through positive values. Equation (8.2.12) thus yields an equation of the form

$$-\frac{d\lambda}{dc} = A + iB, \quad B > 0,$$

or

$$-\frac{dc}{d\lambda} = \frac{dc}{d(\alpha^2)} = \frac{A - iB}{A^2 + B^2}, \quad B > 0. \qquad (8.2.13)$$

Thus, if α^2 *decreases* slightly, c_i becomes *positive*. The existence of a neighbouring unstable solution was first predicted by Tollmien (1935b). The above derivation is a simplified version of a later derivation by Lin (1945).

8.3. A mathematical dilemma

The theory of instability in a perfect fluid has been developed in a fairly complete manner without the use of very complicated mathematical analysis. However, there are two essential difficulties. The first is in the nature of a mathematical dilemma, and will be treated in this section; the second is in the nature of a physical paradox and will be treated in §8.4.

The mathematical difficulty is the following: The solution $\phi_2(y)$ is in general multiple-valued; which branch of the logarithm should be used, especially in the neutral case? This problem is closely related to the assumption—which appears extremely plausible—that the solution of (8.2.1) should be used for the whole real interval (y_1, y_2), if the oscillation is not neutral, since (8.2.1) has no singularity along the real axis. In fact, this assumption specifies the branch of the logarithm to be used in such cases. Consider the case of an oscillation with very little amplification, that is, the case where the imaginary part of c is positive and small. For definiteness, we shall take y_c to be *above* the real axis (real part of w'_c is positive). Then, as the point y passes along the real axis from left to right, the angle of $y - y_c$ *increases* by approximately π. On the other hand, for the damped solution which has a value $c' = c^*$, the point y_c lies *below* the real axis. As the point y moves from left to right, the *angle* of $y - y_{c'}$ *decreases* by approximately π.

If we regard the neutral case as a limit of the self-excited case, we would have, in the expression for $\phi_2(y)$,

$$\log(y - y_c) = \log|y - y_c| - i\pi \quad \text{for} \quad y < y_c, \qquad (8.3.1)$$

if we put $\log(y - y_c) = \log|y - y_c|$ for $y > y_c$. On the other hand, if we regard the neutral case as a limit of the damped case, we would have

$$\log(y - y_c) = \log|y - y_c| + i\pi \quad \text{for} \quad y < y_c. \qquad (8.3.2)$$

Which choice shall we make?

Related to this dilemma is the jump $[W]$, which was calculated for the neutral case by regarding it as a limit of the self-excited case. If we had made the derivation in terms of the *damped* case, we would have obtained *an extra negative sign* in (8.2.8). This is clearly seen from the limiting process described in the second footnote of p. 121.

There is, indeed, no basis for deciding between the two alternatives within the theory of perfect fluids. One then recalls that the fluid is really viscous and that the limiting case of infinite Reynolds number is really under discussion. It then follows from some careful analysis (see §§ 8.4, 8.5) that the *self-excited case is to be used for the limiting process*, as was done in § 8.2.

The damped case, as conceived above, is then not continuously connected with the neutral case, since its limit gives the determination (8.3.2) for $\log(y - y_c)$, while the correct determination is (8.3.1). However, another alternative presents itself. Since we are dealing with a limiting process and not with a perfect fluid *ab initio*, there is no *a priori* reason why the solutions of (8.2.1) should hold for the whole real interval (y_1, y_2), even though it is regular. The validity of a solution must be decided by the criterion that it is a valid asymptotic representation of a solution of (8.1.1). We may continue to take the path below the point y_c in determining the branch of the logarithmic function even in the *damped* case.† We then have a continuity of the solutions, *but the damped and the self-excited solutions are no longer complex conjugates.* Indeed, we must admit that the inviscid damped solution does not hold in the whole interval (y_1, y_2).

This second alternative was proposed by Lin (1944), who reached his conclusions by heuristic analysis and physical arguments. The conclusions are confirmed by the rigorous mathematical analysis of Wasow (1948), who also furnished more complete information regarding the nature of the solutions.

8.4. A physical paradox

If we disregard §8.3 for the moment, and continue to adopt the conclusions reached in §8.2, we find that some of them are also physically paradoxical. The principal one is that damped and self-excited oscillations are complex conjugates. This means that a stable case cannot be characterized by the existence of damped disturbances alone. If such disturbances do exist, their complex conjugates would lead to instability. By adopting the second alternative reached at the end of §8.3, this difficulty is also removed—the existence of damped solutions by no means implies the existence of amplified solutions. We may then expect a clear-cut division, between conditions permitting self-excited disturbance and conditions permitting only damped disturbances, by a state of affairs allowing neutral oscillations.

The actual realization of such a situation may be found in the case of a velocity profile having a point of inflexion and belonging either to the symmetric type or the boundary-layer type. According to §8.2, such a flow allows a neutral disturbance with $\alpha = \alpha_s$, $c = c_s$ (cf. fig. 6.3 a). According to (8.2.13), the neighbouring solutions with $\alpha < \alpha_s$ are self-excited, those with $\alpha > \alpha_s$ are damped. The use of (8.2.13) for damped disturbances implies the adoption of the second alternative of §8.3 in the interpretation of damped disturbances.

† Cf. the specifications in the second paragraph of this section.

If we had adopted the first alternative, we expect a discontinuity between the neutral and damped solutions, and (8.2.13) would not be directly applicable. Indeed, since self-excited disturbances are *not* found for $\alpha > \alpha_s$, damped disturbances, as complex conjugates, would not exist either. On the other hand, for $\alpha < \alpha_s$, disturbances of both kinds exist.

The following table gives a comparison of the conclusions drawn from the two alternative interpretations of damped disturbances:

	$\alpha < \alpha_s$	$\alpha = \alpha_s$	$\alpha > \alpha_s$
First alternative	Disturbances of both kinds are possible	Neutral solution possible	No solution possible
Second alternative	Self-excited	Neutral	Damped
Conclusion from either alternative	Unstable	Neutral	Stable

Thus, although there is no basic difference in the final physical conclusion, the complete exclusion of all disturbances in the stable case shows that the first alternative is not natural.

A more subtle case is presented by the case of velocity profiles without a point of inflexion. Here, neither neutral oscillations nor self-excited oscillations are possible. Damped oscillations are also impossible according to the first alternative, and we conclude that the flow is stable. Are they possible according to the second alternative?

A general answer does not seem to be available; but in certain cases it can be seen definitely that no inviscid solution whatsoever is possible. For example, for plane Couette motion, the inviscid amplitude equation reduces to $\phi'' - \alpha^2\phi = 0$, which certainly does not have a solution vanishing at both ends of the interval y_1 and y_2.

We are forced to conclude that *there are certain damped solutions in a viscous fluid which in the limit of vanishing viscosity, do not reduce to solutions of the inviscid equation throughout the whole region of the flow.* Some detailed studies of certain disturbances belonging to this class are made by C. S. Morawetz (1952) and will not be reproduced here.

8.5. Heuristic approach to the analytical difficulties

A heuristic resolution of the difficulties mentioned above can be based on the formal asymptotic solution described in §8.1. Indeed, it also suggests a way to improve the solutions so that they become valid asymptotic solutions both near to and away from the critical point y_c. We shall therefore present the analysis to motivate the exact treatments in §§ 8.6–8.7.

By the second asymptotic method, we obtain the following four solutions in the initial approximation:

$$\left.\begin{aligned}
&\chi_1^{(0)} = \eta, \quad \chi_2^{(0)} = 1, \\
&\chi_3^{(0)} = \int_{+\infty}^{\eta} d\eta \int_{+\infty}^{\eta} d\eta\, \eta^{\frac{1}{2}} H_{\frac{1}{3}}^{(1)}[\tfrac{2}{3}(i\alpha_0\eta)^{\frac{3}{2}}], \\
&\chi_4^{(0)} = \int_{-\infty}^{\eta} d\eta \int_{-\infty}^{\eta} d\eta\, \eta^{\frac{1}{2}} H_{\frac{1}{3}}^{(2)}[\tfrac{2}{3}(i\alpha_0\eta)^{\frac{3}{2}}],
\end{aligned}\right\} \tag{8.5.1}$$

where $\alpha_0 = (w_c')^{\frac{1}{3}}$. If we continue the solutions to the higher orders, the first two solutions will contain Hankel functions of both kinds. We may anticipate that the asymptotic *expansions* of the solutions (8.5.1) for large η may be comparable with the formal asymptotic *solutions* (8.1.4) and (8.1.6). Indeed, if we carry out the analysis under the restrictions

$$-\tfrac{7}{6}\pi < \arg(\alpha_0\eta) < \tfrac{5}{6}\pi, \tag{8.5.2}$$

we find that

$$\left.\begin{aligned}
&\chi_1^{(0)} + \epsilon\chi_1^{(1)} \sim \eta + \frac{\epsilon w_c''}{2w_c'}\eta^2 + \dots, \\
&\chi_2^{(0)} + \epsilon\chi_2^{(1)} \sim 1 + \epsilon(w_c''/w_c')\,\eta \log \eta + \dots, \\
&\chi_3^{(0)} \sim \text{const.}\, \eta^{-\frac{5}{4}} \exp\{\tfrac{2}{3}(\alpha_0\eta)^{\frac{3}{2}} e^{\frac{5}{4}\pi i}\}, \\
&\chi_4^{(0)} \sim \text{const.}\, \eta^{-\frac{5}{4}} \exp\{\tfrac{2}{3}(\alpha_0\eta)^{\frac{3}{2}} e^{\frac{1}{4}\pi i}\}.
\end{aligned}\right\} \tag{8.5.3}$$

These are immediately comparable with $\phi_1(y)$ and $\phi_2(y)$, as given by (8.1.8), and $\phi_3(y)$ and $\phi_4(y)$ of (8.1.6), provided the negative sign in (8.1.6) is assigned to $\phi_3(y)$ and $(w-c)$ is replaced by the leading terms of its power-series expansion around the critical point y_c.

The restriction (8.5.2) arises naturally if we seek a common region for the asymptotic development of Hankel functions of both kinds and require that this region contains the real axis in the case of real c. If we now accept the above comparison as an indication that the asymptotic solutions (8.1.4) and (8.1.6) are valid under the conditions (8.5.2), the problem of determining the proper branch is solved. On the basis of this conclusion, it is easy to verify the following results: In the neutral case, the correct path to be used around the critical point is *below* the real axis of $w'(y_c) > 0$, and above it if $w'(y_c) < 0$. It also shows that both self-excited and damped disturbances approach the neutral case continuously. In particular, the conclusion is reached that, in the limit of vanishing viscosity, the solution in the self-excited case should be given by a regular solution of (8.1.5) along the real axis, while in the slightly damped case, the inviscid solution must fail somewhere in the interval (y_1, y_2) if y_c belongs to it in the neutral case. In fact, it suggests the breakdown at two points (y'_f, y''_f), where the lines $\arg(\alpha_0 \eta) = -\frac{7}{6}\pi$ and $\arg(\alpha_0 \eta) = \frac{1}{6}\pi$ intersect the real axis. The significance of these points will be discussed in §8.8. Arguments along the above line were used by Lin (1944).

The comparison of (8.5.3) with the first asymptotic solutions depends on the approximation

$$\tfrac{2}{3}(\alpha_0 \eta)^{\frac{3}{2}} e^{\frac{5}{4}\pi i} \cong -(\alpha R)^{\frac{1}{2}} Q,$$

that is,

$$\alpha_0 \eta \cong \left[\frac{3}{2} \int_{y_c}^{y} \sqrt{\{\alpha R(w - c)\}}\, dy\right]^{\frac{2}{3}}.$$

If we now simply make this *replacement* in $\chi_3^{(0)}$ and $\chi_4^{(0)}$, and make a suitable adjustment to take care of the term $f_0(y)$ in (8.1.6), we should obtain solutions which are adequate for finite values of y and finite values of η. Indeed, these modified solutions are

$$\left. \begin{aligned}
\chi_3^{(0)} &= \left(\frac{\zeta}{w - c}\right)^{\frac{5}{4}} \int_{+\infty}^{\zeta} d\zeta \int_{+\infty}^{\zeta} d\zeta \cdot \zeta^{\frac{1}{2}} H_{\frac{1}{3}}^{(1)} [\tfrac{2}{3}(i\zeta)^{\frac{3}{2}}], \\
\chi_4^{(0)} &= \left(\frac{\zeta}{w - c}\right)^{\frac{5}{4}} \int_{-\infty}^{\zeta} d\zeta \int_{-\infty}^{\zeta} d\zeta\, \zeta^{\frac{1}{2}} H_{\frac{1}{3}}^{(2)} [\tfrac{2}{3}(i\zeta)^{\frac{3}{2}}],
\end{aligned} \right\} \tag{8.5.4}$$

where

$$\zeta = (\alpha R)^{\frac{1}{3}} \left[\frac{3}{2} \int_{y_c}^{y} \sqrt{(w - c)}\, dy\right]^{\frac{2}{3}}. \tag{8.5.5}$$

Let us now return to the solutions $\phi_1(y)$ and $\phi_2(y)$ in the form (8.1.8). It is plausible that $\phi_1(y)$ does not need any modification. For $\phi_2(y)$ the comparison of (8.1.8) with (8.5.3) suggests the replacement of the logarithmic term by $\epsilon \chi_2^{(1)}$, whose asymptotic expansion is $\epsilon(w''_c / w'_c) \eta \log \eta$ comparable to

$$(w''_c / w'_c)(y - y_c)[\log(y - y_c) + \text{const.}].$$

Thus, we arrive at the solution

$$\phi_2(y) = 1 + \ldots + \epsilon \chi_2^{(1)} P(y - y_c) / P(0), \tag{8.5.6}$$

where the first part is the corresponding power series in (8.1.8). Asymptotically, this solution is comparable to (8.1.8); for small values of $y - y_c$ it agrees with (8.5.3).

The improved solutions (8.5.4) and (8.5.6) were first obtained by Tollmien (1947), who also proved their asymptotic validity, for real values of c and y, without the restrictions discussed in §8.1 on the first two asymptotic methods. Note that $\phi_2(y)$ is regular at the critical point y_c.

As mentioned before, there is yet no algorism for continuing solutions of this type to higher approximations. In many physical problems, this is not necessary.

Solutions of a similar nature have been obtained by Wasow (1953b) for complex values of c and y. These will be discussed in detail in §8.7.

8.6. Asymptotic solutions of the first kind

We shall now present the complete theory for asymptotic solutions of the first kind, which are adequate for characteristic-value problems of class I (p. 118). The conclusions will be found to corroborate those obtained by the heuristic methods described above, but further information about those solutions is found by the exact analysis.

Since the solutions (8.1.4) and (8.1.6) are expected to be valid for fixed y, they may be used at the end-points y_1 and y_2 for the purpose of satisfying the conditions (8.1.2), if y_c does not approach either one of these points. The chief difficulty is then associated with the critical point y_c. It is well known that, around such a point, the asymptotic expression for a *given* solution often takes on *different* forms for various sectors of the complex plane ('Stokes phenomenon'). One of the central issues is then the determination of the proper transition of the asymptotic expressions. A more subtle issue is to prove that the formal asymptotic solutions are indeed the asymptotic representations of certain actual solutions of (8.1.1).

A complete theory of this problem has been given by Wasow (1948). We shall not give a direct account of his theory here. Rather, we shall outline some of his conclusions which are of interest to the problem of hydrodynamic stability. In order to bring out the significance of his conclusions more clearly, we shall present our discussion in two parts. In the first part, attention will be directed to obtaining solutions suitable for solving the characteristic-value problem. In the second part, attention will be directed to the complete behaviour of the solutions, especially the one which is asymptotically represented by the solution $\phi_2(y)$ in (8.1.8).

(i) *Valid asymptotic solutions.* Wasow has shown that the region of validity† of the asymptotic solutions (8.1.4) and (8.1.6) are both determined by the lines $\mathrm{Re}\,(Q) = \mathrm{const}$. Such lines branch off from

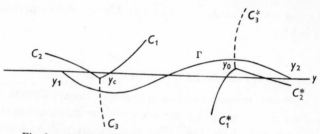

Fig. 8.1. Diagram showing region of validity of asymptotic solutions (after Foote and Lin, 1950).

critical points y_c, with three branches at equal angles through each such point. A typical geometry is shown in fig. 8.1, which corresponds to the case of a velocity distribution for a jet. The points y_c and y_0 are the critical points.

The following conclusion can be easily drawn from Wasow's theorems: *If any two points of a region can be connected by a curve along which $\mathrm{Re}\,(Q)$ changes monotonically, the asymptotic solutions (8.1.4) and (8.1.6) are valid in that region.*‡ In many problems of hydrodynamic stability, such a region includes the end-points where the boundary conditions are to be imposed (see fig. 8.1). Thus, in such problems, there is *no need for changing* the asymptotic representation of a given solution. To this extent, the present problem is simpler than a similar one in quantum mechanics.

† This means a region in which a given solution is represented by the same asymptotic expression.

‡ See Foote and Lin (1950).

(ii) *Asymptotic behaviour of solutions in the third sector.* Consider now the neighbourhood of a single critical point, say y_c, and the four formal asymptotic series

$$\left.\begin{aligned}
\phi_1 &= \phi_1^{(0)} + (\alpha R)^{-1} \phi_1^{(1)} + (\alpha R)^{-2} \phi_1^{(2)} + \ldots, \\
\phi_2 &= \phi_2^{(0)} + (\alpha R)^{-1} \phi_2^{(1)} + (\alpha R)^{-2} \phi_2^{(2)} + \ldots, \\
\phi_3 &= \{\exp[-(\alpha R)^{\frac{1}{2}} Q(y)]\}\{(w-c)^{-\frac{5}{4}} + O(\alpha R)^{-\frac{1}{2}}\}, \\
\phi_4 &= \{\exp[+(\alpha R)^{\frac{1}{2}} Q(y)]\}\{(w-c)^{-\frac{5}{4}} + O(\alpha R)^{-\frac{1}{2}}\},
\end{aligned}\right\}$$

where $\phi_1^{(0)}$ and $\phi_2^{(0)}$ are the first and the second of the inviscid solutions (8.1.8). Now, Wasow has shown that there are actual solutions with these asymptotic representations in the sectors S_1 and S_2 opposite to C_1 and C_2. The question is: What are their behaviours in the sector S_3 opposite to C_3?

Such a question is best answered by the following theorems of Wasow. Consider a neighbourhood $0 < \delta \leqslant |y - y_c| \leqslant a$, where δ is an arbitrary small but fixed positive number and a is a suitable positive number.

(1) There is a solution which is asymptotically represented by $\phi_1(y)$ for all three sectors.

(2) There is a solution which is asymptotically represented by $\phi_2(y)$ for the sectors S_1 and S_2; but in the sector S_3, such a solution must take on the nature of ϕ_3 or ϕ_4 with a *positive* real part for $Q(y)$.

(3) There is a solution which is asymptotically represented by $\phi_3(y)$ in the sectors S_1 and S_2; this solution is still asymptotically represented by $\phi_3(y)$ in S_3, if it is interpreted as a continuation from the sector S_2 across the curve C_1; that is, if $\mathrm{Re}(Q)$ increases as the point enters the sector S_3.

(4) There is a solution which is asymptotically represented by $\phi_4(y)$ in the sectors S_1 and S_2; this solution is still asymptotically represented by $\phi_4(y)$ in S_3, if it is interpreted as a continuation from the sector S_1 across the curve C_2; that is, if $\mathrm{Re}(Q)$ increases as the point enters the sector S_3.

The most interesting of these results is the asymptotic solution $\phi_2(y)$ which must be continued into the sector S_3 by a 'viscous' solution, although it is 'non-viscous' in the sectors S_1 and S_2. The complete picture of the 'viscous' effect is therefore represented by the shaded portion in fig. 8.2. The small circle represents the region where all the asymptotic representations are not known to be valid. From the second method described in §8.1, this region has a radius of the order of $\epsilon = (\alpha R)^{-\frac{1}{3}}$.

8.7. The improved asymptotic solutions

The improved asymptotic solutions, as given by Tollmien for real values of c and y, have been described in §8.5. We shall now

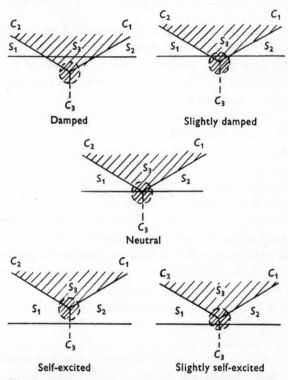

Damped

Slightly damped

Neutral

Self-excited

Slightly self-excited

Fig. 8.2. Geometry of a complete neighbourhood of the critical point; 'viscous regions' are shaded.

present the solutions given by Wasow (1953b) for general values of c and y. The solutions are valid in a finite region containing the critical point.

Instead of following his paper literally, the solutions will be given for the special differential equation (8.1.1). The essence of the method is of course preserved.

We have seen that in the sectors S_1 and S_2 a fundamental system of asymptotic solutions of (8.1.1) is

$$
\left.
\begin{aligned}
\phi_1^{(0)}(y) &= (y-y_c)\,P(y-y_c), \\
\phi_2^{(0)}(y) &= \tilde{P}(y-y_c) + \frac{w_c''}{w_c'}\,\phi_1^{(0)}(y)\log(y-y_c), \\
\phi_3^{(0)}(y) &= (w-c)^{-\frac{5}{4}}\exp\left\{-\int_{y_c}^{y}\sqrt{\{i\alpha R(w-c)\}}\,dy\right\}, \\
\phi_4^{(0)}(y) &= (w-c)^{-\frac{5}{4}}\exp\left\{+\int_{y_c}^{y}\sqrt{\{i\alpha R(w-c)\}}\,dy\right\},
\end{aligned}
\right\}
\tag{8.7.1}
$$

where
$$
\left.
\begin{aligned}
P(y-y_c) &= 1 + \frac{w_c''}{2w_c'}(y-y_c)+\dots, \\
\tilde{P}(y-y_c) &= 1 + b_1(y-y_c)+\dots.
\end{aligned}
\right\}
\tag{8.7.2}
$$

Let us now consider the equation

$$
\frac{d^4F}{dz^4} + \lambda^2(zF''+F) = 0, \quad \lambda^2 = -i\alpha R,
\tag{8.7.3}
$$

which is simpler than (8.1.1), but has some of its general features. The asymptotic solutions of (8.7.3) corresponding to (8.7.1) are

$$
\left.
\begin{aligned}
F_1^{(0)}(z) &= z^{\frac{1}{2}}J_1(2z^{\frac{1}{2}}) = z - \tfrac{1}{2}z^2 + \dots, \\
F_2^{(0)}(z) &= \pi i z^{\frac{1}{2}}H_1^{(1)}(2z^{\frac{1}{2}}) = 1 + zP_2(z) - F_1^{(0)}(z)\log z, \\
F_3^{(0)}(z) &= z^{-\frac{5}{4}}\exp\left\{-\sqrt{(i\alpha R)}\,\tfrac{2}{3}z^{\frac{3}{2}}\right\}, \\
F_4^{(0)}(z) &= z^{-\frac{5}{4}}\exp\left\{+\sqrt{(i\alpha R)}\,\tfrac{2}{3}z^{\frac{3}{2}}\right\},
\end{aligned}
\right\}
\tag{8.7.4}
$$

valid in a corresponding domain in the z-plane. To bring these solutions into as close an agreement with (8.7.1) as possible, we put

$$
\left.
\begin{aligned}
z &= -(w_c''/w_c')(y-y_c) \quad \text{in} \quad F_1^{(0)}(z),\ F_2^{(0)}(z); \\
z &= \left\{\frac{3}{2}\int_{y_c}^{y}\sqrt{(w-c)}\,dy\right\}^{\frac{2}{3}} \quad \text{in} \quad F_3^{(0)}(z),\ F_4^{(0)}(z).
\end{aligned}
\right\}
\tag{8.7.5}
$$

Indeed, we have the following correspondence for the first two functions

$$
\left.
\begin{aligned}
F_1^{(0)}(z) &\sim \psi_1^{(0)} = -(w_c''/w_c')\,\phi_1^{(0)}(y), \\
F_2^{(0)}(z) &\sim \psi_2^{(0)} = \phi_2^{(0)}(y) + (w_c''/w_c')\,\phi_1^{(0)}(y)\log(-w_c''/w_c').
\end{aligned}
\right\}
\tag{8.7.6}
$$

The solutions corresponding to $F_3^{(0)}(z)$ and $F_4^{(0)}(z)$ differ from $\phi_3^{(0)}(y)$ and $\phi_4^{(0)}(y)$ by some obvious factors.

Now, the exact solutions of (8.7.3) can be calculated by the method of Laplace's transformation, and it is possible to find a fundamental system of such solutions with the asymptotic behaviour (8.7.4). Suppose that the exact solutions $F_i(z)$ behave asymptotically as $F_i^{(0)}(z)$ in the sectors S_1 and S_2 of the y-plane, z being related to y by (8.7.5). Denote by $\psi_i^{(0)}(y)$ the asymptotic solutions of (8.1.1) corresponding to $F_i^{(0)}(z)$, that is, $\psi_1^{(0)}(y)$, $\psi_2^{(0)}(y)$ are given by the expressions in (8.7.6) and $\psi_3^{(0)}(y)$, $\psi_4^{(0)}(y)$ are given by $\phi_3^{(0)}(y)$, $\phi_4^{(0)}(y)$. Clearly

$$\psi_i = \{\psi_i^{(0)}(y)/F_i^{(0)}(z)\} F_i(z) \qquad (8.7.7)$$

is also an asymptotic solution in the sectors S_1 and S_2. But the important point is that these solutions may be shown to hold *in a larger region*. Indeed, except for $\psi_2^{(0)}/F_2^{(0)}$ all the ratios $\psi_i^{(0)}/F_i^{(0)}$ are independent of αR and are *regular* in a complete neighbourhood of the critical point y_c. Even with $\psi_2^{(0)}/F_2^{(0)}$ the singularity has become as weak as that in $1 + O[(y-y_c)^2 \log (y-y_c)]$.

The complete proof of the validity of this construction has been given by Wasow (1953 b), who gave detailed estimates of the errors of the approximate solutions (8.7.7) together with their first derivatives.

It is clear that the second derivative of $\psi_2(y)$ as defined by (8.7.7) diverges at the critical point. This could be avoided by the following alternative construction: We note that $\psi_2^{(0)}(y)$ can be split into the two parts

$$\left. \begin{aligned} \psi_{2a}^{(0)}(y) &= R(y-y_c), \\ \psi_{2b}^{(0)}(y) &= (w_c''/w_c') \phi_1^{(0)}(y) \log [(-w_c''/w_c')(y-y_c)], \end{aligned} \right\} \qquad (8.7.8)$$

where the first part is regular (cf. (8.7.1)), while the second part is singular. A corresponding decomposition can be made for $F_2^{(0)}(z)$. We then construct the *regular* function

$$\Psi_2(y) = \psi_{2a}^{(0)}(y) + \{\psi_{2b}^{(0)}(y)/F_{2b}^{(0)}(z)\} F_{2b}(z), \qquad (8.7.9)$$

where (cf. (8.7.4))

$$\left. \begin{aligned} F_{2a}^{(0)}(z) &= 1 + zP_2(z), \quad F_{2b}^{(0)}(z) = -F_1^{(0)}(z) \log z, \\ F_{2b}(z) &= F_2(z) - F_{2a}^{(0)}(z). \end{aligned} \right\} \qquad (8.7.10)$$

Again it is clear that $\Psi_2(y)$ has the asymptotic behaviour $\psi_2^{(0)}(y)$. It also has the desired feature of being regular.

Both Tollmien and Wasow have obtained error estimates for their solutions. Except for the second solution, errors no larger than $O(\epsilon)$ are incurred in the functions and their first derivatives. In the case of the second solution, the error is no larger than ϵ, in the function. But for the first derivative, which is itself of the order $\log \epsilon$ for $y - y_c$ of the order ϵ, the corresponding error estimate is of the order of $\log \epsilon$ in Tollmien's estimate for the real case, and of the order of unity in Wasow's estimate for the general complex case. Di Prima (1954), however, has verified that, in the real case, Wasow's solution, together with the first derivative, agree with Tollmien's with errors no larger than those given by Tollmien's estimate. The same conclusion applies to the solution (8.7.9). It is then plausible that Wasow's error estimate can be improved even in the complex case. For this purpose there might be some advantage in using the regular modified solution (8.7.9).

8.8. Friction layers and friction regions

The analytical nature of the solutions can be more vividly described in terms of the effect of viscosity in certain layers and regions when the Reynolds number becomes very large. As it is familiar in the case of ordinary boundary-layer theory, the effect of viscosity is often limited in a certain *thin layer whose thickness approaches zero* as the Reynolds number becomes infinite. On the other hand, we shall find that, in our case, the viscous effect may extend over a finite *region* in the fluid whose thickness does *not* approach zero in the limit of infinite Reynolds number.

To describe such viscous behaviour, it is again convenient to divide the problem into the two classes discussed in §8.1:

Class I: Cases in which the critical point does not approach either of the end-points in the limit

Class II: Cases in which the critical point approaches one of the end-points in the limit

(i) Class I. In these cases, it is sufficient to use asymptotic solutions studied in §8.6. Excluding the case of very highly damped solutions, the solution of the characteristic-value problem approaches an inviscid solution in the limit. For large values of αR, the modification near the boundary is associated with viscous solutions with the exponential term $\exp[\pm\sqrt{(\alpha R)}\,Q]$. The viscous region then extends over a distance of the order of $(\alpha R)^{-\frac{1}{2}}$, whose thickness approaches zero as $\alpha R \to \infty$. This is often referred to as the *outer viscous layer*.

An *inner viscous region* is expected to be associated with the critical point y_c. In general, it depends on the geometry of the real axis and the lines $\mathrm{Re}\,(Q)=0$, as studied in §8.6. Referring to fig. 8.2, where the shaded regions are viscous, we may summarize the results as follows:

(1) The outer and inner viscous layers or regions are distinctly separated from each other for αR sufficiently large.

(2) The outer viscous layer has a thickness of the order of magnitude of $(\alpha R)^{-\frac{1}{2}}$ approaching zero as $\alpha R \to \infty$.

(3) In the case of finite amplification, there is no inner viscous layer for sufficiently large values of the Reynolds number, that is, for $(\alpha R)^{-\frac{1}{3}} \ll c_i$.

(4) In the case of finite damping, there is a viscous *region* of finite width, however large the value of αR may become.

(5) In the neutral case, the thickness of the viscous layer is of the order of $(\alpha R)^{-\frac{1}{3}}$, and approaches zero as $\alpha R \to \infty$.

(6) In the cases of damped and amplified disturbances with $|c_i| = O(\alpha R)^{-\frac{1}{3}}$—and hence approaching zero as $\alpha R \to \infty$—the disturbance has a behaviour similar to the neutral cases.

All the above statements are made with the provision $w''(y_c) \neq 0$. The case $w''(y_c)=0$ has been treated in some detail by Wasow (1953a). The reader is referred to his paper for the details.

It should be emphasized that the viscous effect is to be associated with the whole third sector S_3, besides a circular region around the critical point y_c. The latter has a radius of the order of $(\alpha R)^{-\frac{1}{3}}$ and approaches zero as $\alpha R \to \infty$. In the physical interpretation, one should therefore distinguish between a viscous *layer* and a viscous *region* of finite width. In the heuristic discussion of §8.5, only two viscous *layers*, at y_f' and y_f'', are indicated. What happens in between is not known until the full theory is developed (see §8.6). The existence of the viscous layers is then confirmed with the further information that the entire *region in between* is viscous.

Statement (6) above stresses clearly the importance of recognizing different limiting processes. No matter how small c_i may be, so long as it is finite, the limiting case $\alpha R \to \infty$ is to be covered by statements (3) and (4). On the other hand, if c_i goes to zero faster than $(\alpha R)^{-\frac{1}{3}}$, statement (6) applies.†

(ii) *Class II.* A detailed description of class II is very complicated. For definiteness, let us first consider the lower and upper branches of the neutral curve in the case of the plane Poiseuille motion.

(a) *Lower branch of the neutral curve.* Along this curve, the value of

$$\eta_1 = (y_1 - y_c)(\alpha R)^{\frac{1}{3}}$$

approaches a finite limit as $\alpha R \to \infty$. Thus, the boundary point y_1 lies at a distance of the order of $\epsilon = (\alpha R)^{-\frac{1}{3}}$ from the critical point y_c, and therefore essentially within the circular viscous region around y_c (fig. 8.2). There is no distinction between inner and outer friction layers. There is a single viscous layer which extends from the solid boundary to the critical point $y = y_c$ and *whose thickness approaches* zero as $\alpha R \to \infty$.

The same general conclusions hold for damped or amplified disturbances if the complex variable η_1 approaches a finite limit as $\alpha R \to \infty$. It should be emphasized that in the limit of infinite Reynolds number the disturbance approaches a steady-state deviation with $c = 0$. There is no distinction between amplified, damped or neutral oscillations in the limit.

However, it is possible for the characteristic value c to approach zero in a somewhat different manner, as happens in the next case.

(b) *Upper branch of the neutral curve.* Along the upper branch, the value of

$$\eta_1 = (y_1 - y_c)(\alpha R)^{\frac{1}{3}}$$

becomes infinite as $\alpha R \to \infty$. However, $y_1 - y_c$ still approaches zero. In fact, for plane Poiseuille motion

$$\left.\begin{array}{l} \eta_1 \sim (\alpha R)^{\frac{2}{15}}, \\ y_1 - y_c \sim (\alpha R)^{-\frac{1}{5}}. \end{array}\right\}$$

Note that η_1 is the ratio of the distance $y_1 - y_c$ to the thickness of the friction layer (radius of the circular region around the point y_c).

† For a brief account of the misunderstandings that had arisen in connexion with the outer and inner viscous regions, see Lin (1954a, § 10).

Thus we may still regard the outer and inner friction layers as separated from each other.

The above are relatively simple cases. In the case of amplified and damped solutions, the condition $y_c \to y_1$ implies $c_r \to 0$ and $c_i \to 0$. The exact manner in which these two limiting processes depend on the Reynolds number αR may still vary, and this leads to descriptions of the inner and outer friction layers somewhat different from the above. We shall not go into the details of such discussions here.

8.9. Concluding remarks

The above discussions serve to illustrate the difficulties in the limiting process. It is necessary that these be completely understood; otherwise, one would wonder what happens in the limit of αR becoming infinite if one follows a path of constant α in fig. 3.1. Obviously, the limiting point must correspond to a damped solution, but we know that the inviscid equation does not have a damped solution valid along the real axis. The above discussions show that the limit of a solution with finite damping does not satisfy the inviscid solution along the whole section of the real axis corresponding to the fluid field (except possibly in the exceptional case of $w''(y_c) = 0$), and consequently the effect of viscosity does not become negligible in such limiting processes of vanishing viscosity.

Two important reasons may be suggested for the cause of the complication in the discussion of the limiting process:

(1) Different limiting processes are often involved, with different results. This is clearly seen by contrasting the various cases discussed in §8.8.

(2) The solution $\phi_2(y)$ has an unusual behaviour, as explained in §8.6. Without realizing this, one would have associated the viscous effects solely with the circular neighbourhood of the size $(\alpha R)^{-\frac{1}{3}}$ around the critical point y_c. The difficulty in the formal limiting process, discussed in §§8.3 and 8.4, would then appear.

Finally, it may be remarked that the behaviour of the solution with finite damping closely resembles the structure of turbulence discussed by Batchelor and Townsend.† The fluid motion exhibits

† G. K. Batchelor and A. A. Townsend, *Proc. Roy. Soc.* A, **99**, 238–55 (1949).

a highly oscillatory behaviour over a finite part of the field and very slow changes in another part. This again demonstrates an often stressed fundamental property of the motion of viscous fluids at high Reynolds numbers. In certain cases, the fluid behaves as a perfect fluid; in other cases, the effect of viscosity cannot be neglected even if it is very small. The increasingly refined spatial structure of the fluid motion is just enough to counterbalance the vanishing of viscosity and to maintain the effects of the viscous terms in the Navier–Stokes equations of motion.

BIBLIOGRAPHY

BASSETT, A. B. (1893). Stability and instability of viscous fluids. *Proc. Roy. Soc.* A, **52**, 273–6.

BATEMAN, H. (1932). Article in *Hydrodynamics* by H. L. Dryden, F. D. Murnaghan and H. Bateman. *Bull. Nat. Res. Coun., Wash.*, **84**, 372–82.

BATTIN, R. H. (1950). On the stability of the boundary layer over a body of revolution. *Proc. Int. Congr. Math.* p. 625.

BATTIN, R. H. and LIN, C. C. (1950). On the stability of the boundary layer over a cone. *J. Aero. Sci.* **17**, 453.

BELYAKOVA, V. K. (1950). Concerning the stability of the motion of a viscous fluid in a straight circular tube. *Akad. Nauk. S.S.S.R. Prikl. Math. Meh.* **14**, 105–10.

BÉNARD, M. (1901). Les troubillions cellulaires dans une nappe liquide transportant de la chaleur par convection en régime permanent. *Ann. Chim. (Phys.)*, **23**, 62–144.

BERSON, F. A. (1949). Summary of a theoretical investigation into the factors controlling the instability of long waves in zonal currents. *Tellus*, **1**, 44–52.

BLOOM, M. (1951). The effect of surface cooling on laminar boundary-layer stability. *J. Aero. Sci.* **18**, 635–6.

BLOOM, M. (1952). Further comments on 'The effect of surface cooling on laminar boundary-layer stability'. *J. Aero. Sci.* **19**, 359.

BLOOM, M. (1954). On the calculation of laminar boundary-layer stability. *J. Aero. Sci.* **21**, 207–10.

BLUMENTHAL, O. (1913). On the problem of turbulence. *S.B. bayer. Akad. Wiss.* pp. 563–5.

BUSSMANN, K. and MÜNZ, H. (1942). Die Stabilität der laminar Reibungsschicht mit Absaugung. *Jb. dtsch. Luftfahrtf. Zbl. wiss. Ber.-Wes.* **1**, 35.

BUSSMANN, K. and ULRICH, A. (1943). Systematic investigations of the influence of the shape of the profile upon the position of the transition point. *N.A.C.A.* TM 1185, 51 pp.; translated from *Jb. dtsch. Luftfahrtf.* 1943, p. 1.

CHANDRA, K. (1938). Instability of fluids heated from below. *Proc. Roy. Soc.* A, **164**, 231–42.

CHANDRASEKHAR, S. (1952a). On the inhibition of convection by a magnetic fluid. *Phil. Mag.* (7), **43**, 501–32.

CHANDRASEKHAR, S. (1952b). The thermal instability of a fluid sphere heated within. *Phil. Mag.* (7), **43**, 1317–29.

CHANDRASEKHAR, S. (1953a). The onset of convection by thermal instability in spherical shells. *Phil. Mag.* (7), **44**, 233–41, 1129–30.

CHANDRASEKHAR, S. (1953b). The stability of viscous flow between rotating cylinders in the presence of a magnetic field. *Proc. Roy. Soc.* A, **216**, 293–309.

CHANDRASEKHAR, S. (1953c). The instability of a layer of fluid heated below and subject to Coriolis forces. *Proc. Roy. Soc.* A, **217**, 306–27.

CHANDRASEKHAR, S. (1954a). The gravitational instability of an infinite homogeneous medium when Coriolis force is acting and a magnetic field is present. *Astrophys. J.* **119**, 7–9.

CHANDRASEKHAR, S. (1954b). The stability of viscous flow between rotating cylinders in the presence of a radial temperature gradient. *J. Rat. Mech. Analy.* **3**, 181–207.

CHANDRASEKHAR, S. (1954c). The instability of a layer of fluid heated below and subject to simultaneous action of magnetic field and rotation. *Proc. Roy. Soc.* A, **225**, 173–84.

CHANDRASEKHAR, S. (1954d). Examples of the instability of fluid motion in the presence of a magnetic field. *Proc. 5th Symp. Appl. Math.* (AMS), pp. 19–27.

CHANDRASEKHAR, S. (1954e). The stability of viscous flow between rotating cylinders. *Mathematika*, **1**, 5–13.

CHANDRASEKHAR, S. and FERMI, E. (1953). Problems of gravitational stability in the presence of a magnetic field. *Astrophys. J.* **118**, 116–41.

CHARNEY, J. G. (1947). The dynamics of long waves in a baroclinic westerly current. *J. Met.* **4**, 135–62.

CHARNEY, J. G. (1948). On the scale of atmospheric motions. *Geofys. Publ.* **17**, no. 2, 17 pp.

CHENG, S. I. (1953). On the stability of laminar boundary layer flow. *Quart. Appl. Math.* **11**, 346–50.

CHIARULLI, P. (1949). *Stability of Two-dimensional Velocity Distribution of the Half-jet Type.* Tech. Rep. no. F-TS/1228-IA, Headquarters Air Material Command, Wright-Patterson Air Force Base, iv + 51 pp.

CHIARULLI, P. and FREEMAN, J. C. (1948). *Stability of the Boundary Layer.* Tech. Rep. no. F-TR/1197-IA, Headquarters Air Material Command, Dayton, 104 pp.

COWLING, T. G. (1951). The condition for turbulence in rotating stars. *Astrophys. J.* **114**, 272–86.

CURLE, N. (1953). The mechanics of edge tones. *Proc. Roy. Soc.* A, **216**, 412–24.

CZARNECKI, K. R. and SINCLAIR, A. R. (1953). Factors affecting transition at supersonic speeds. *N.A.C.A.* RM L53118a.

CZARNECKI, K. R. and SINCLAIR, A. R. (1954a). Preliminary investigation of the effects of heat transfer on boundary-layer transition on a parabolic body of revolution at a Mach number of 1·61. *Rep. N.A.C.A.* TN 3165.

CZARNECKI, K. R. and SINCLAIR, A. R. (1954b). An extension of the investigation of the effects of heat transfer on boundary-layer transition on a parabolic body of revolution at a Mach number of 1·61. *N.A.C.A.* TN 3166.

DEAN, W. R. (1928). Fluid motion in a curved channel. *Proc. Roy. Soc.* A, **121**, 402–20.

DI PRIMA, R. C. (1954). A note on the asymptotic solutions of the equation of hydrodynamic stability. *J. Math. Phys.* **33**, 249.

DI PRIMA, R. C. (1955). Application of the Galerkin method to the calculation of the stability of curved flows. *Quart. Appl. Math.* **13**, 55–62.

DRYDEN, H. L. (1948). Recent advances in the mechanics of boundary-layer flow. *Advanc. Appl. Mech.* 1.

DRYDEN, H. L. (1953). Review of published data on the effect of roughness on transition from laminar to turbulent flow. *J. Aero. Sci.* 29, 477–82.

DRYDEN, H. L., SCHUBAUER, G. B., MOCK, W. C., Jr., and SKRAMSTAD, H. K. (1937). Measurements of intensity and scale of wind-tunnel turbulence and their relation to the critical Reynolds number of spheres. *N.A.C.A. Tech. Rep.* no. 581.

DUNN, D. W. (1953). On the stability of the boundary layer in a compressible fluid. Doctorate dissertation, Massachusetts Institute of Technology.

DUNN, D. W. and LIN, C. C. (1952). The stability of the laminary boundary layer in a compressible fluid for the case of three-dimensional disturbances. *J. Aero. Sci.* 19, 491.

DUNN, D. W. and LIN, C. C. (1953). On the role of three-dimensional disturbances in the stability of supersonic boundary layers. *J. Aero. Sci.* 20, 577.

DUNN, D. W. and LIN, C. C. (1955). On the stability of the laminar boundary layer in a compressible fluid. *J. Aero. Sci.* 22, 455–77.

EADY, E. T. (1949). Long waves and cyclone waves. *Tellus*, 1, 33–52.

EMMONS, H. W. (1951). The laminar-turbulent transition in a boundary layer. *J. Aero. Sci.* 18, 490–8.

EVVARD, J. C., TUCKER, M. and BURGESS, W. C. (1954). Statistical study of transition-point fluctuations in supersonic flow. *N.A.C.A. Rep.* TN 3100.

FAGE, A. (1938). The influence of wall oscillations, wall rotation and entry eddies on the breakdown of laminar flow in an annular pipe. *Proc. Roy. Soc.* A, 165, 513–17.

FAGE, A. and PRESTON, J. H. (1941). On transition from laminar to turbulent flow in the boundary layer. *Proc. Roy. Soc.* A, 178, 201–27.

FAXEN, H. (1928). Konvergenz Untersuchungen zu G. I. Taylors Abhandlung über die Stabilität der Bewegungen einer zähen Flussigkeit zwischen zwei rotierenden Zylindern. *Ark. Mat. Astr. Fys.* 21A, no. 26, 1–11.

FJØRTOFT, R. (1950). Application of integral theorems in deriving criteria of stability for laminar flows and for the baroclinic circular vortex. *Geofys. Publ.* 17, no. 5, 52 pp.

FJØRTOFT, R. (1951). Stability properties of large-scale atmospheric disturbances. *Compendium Meteor.*, pp. 454–63, Amer. Meteor. Soc., Boston, 1950.

FOOTE, J. R. and LIN, C. C. (1950). Some recent investigations in the theory of hydrodynamic stability. *Quart. Appl. Math.* 8, 265–80.

FRIEDRICHS, K. O. (1942). *Fluid Dynamics* (mimeographed lecture notes, Brown University, 1942), ch. IV, pp. 200–209.

GAMBO, K. (1950). The criteria for stability of the westerlies. *Geophys. Notes, Tokyo,* 3, 1–13.

GAZLEY, C. (1953). Boundary-layer stability and transition in subsonic and supersonic flow. *J. Aero. Sci.* 20, 19–28.

GOLDSTEIN, S. (1936). The stability of viscous fluid flow under pressure between parallel plates. *Proc. Camb. Phil. Soc.* **32**, 40–54.

GOLDSTEIN, S. (1937). The stability of viscous flow between rotating cylinders. *Proc. Camb. Phil. Soc.* **33**, 41–61.

GOLDSTEIN, S. (ed.) (1938). *Modern Developments in Fluid Dynamics.* Oxford: Clarendon Press, esp. pp. 135–6, 157, 194–200, 564.

GÖRTLER, H. (1940a). Über den Einfluss der Wandkrummung auf die Entstehung der Turbulenz. *Z. angew. Math. Mech.* **20**, 138–47.

GÖRTLER, H. (1940b). Über eine dreidimensionale Instabilität laminarer Grenzschichten an konkaven Wanden. *Nachr. Ges. Wiss. Göttingen,* N.F., **2**, no. 1, pp. 1–26.

GÖRTLER, H. (1941). Instabilität laminarer Grenzschichten an konkaven Wänden gegenüber gewissen drei-dimensionalen Störungen. *Z. angew. Math. Mech.* **21**, 250–2.

GREGORY, N., STUART, J. T., and WALKER, W. S. (1955). On the stability of three-dimensional boundary layers with application to the flow due to a rotating disk. *Phil. Trans.* A, **248**, 155–99.

GROHNE, D. (1954). Über das Spektrum bei Eigenschwingungen ebener Laminarströmungen. *Z. angew. Math. Mech.* **35**, 344–57.

HAHNEMAN, E., FREEMAN, J. C. and FINSTON, M. (1948). Stability of boundary layers and of flow in entrance section of a channel. *J. Aero. Sci.* **15**, 493–6.

HALL, A. A. and HISLOP, G. S. (1938). Experiments on the transition of the laminar bounary layer on a flat plate. *Rep. Memor. Aero. Res. Comm., Lond.,* no. 1843.

HAMEL, G. (1911). Zum Turbulenzproblem. *Nachr. Ges. Wiss. Göttingen,* pp. 261–70.

HAMMERLIN, G. (1955). Uber das Eigenwertproblem der drei-dimensionalen Instabilität laminarer Grenzschichten an konkaven Wänden. *J. Rat. Mech. Analysis,* **4**, 279–321.

HARRISON, W. H. (1921). On the stability of the steady motion of viscous liquid contained between rotating coaxial cylinders. *Proc. Camb. Phil. Soc.* **20**, 455–9.

HAUPT, O. (1912). Über die Entwicklung einer willkürlichen Funktion nach den Eigenfunktionen des Turbulenzproblems. *S.B. bayer. Akad. Wiss.* pp. 289–301.

HAVELOCK, T. H. (1921). The stability of fluid motion. *Proc. Roy. Soc.* A, **98**, 428–37.

HEISENBERG, W. (1924). Über Stabilität und Turbulenz von Flüssigkeitsströmen. *Ann. Phys., Lpz.,* (4), **74**, 577–627.

HEISENBERG, W. (1950). On the stability of laminar flow. *Proc. Int. Congr. Math.* pp. 292–6.

HIGGINS, R. W. and PAPPAS, C. C. (1951). An experimental investigation of the effect of surface heating on boundary-layer transition on a flat plate in supersonic flow. *N.A.C.A.* TN 2351.

HOLLINGDALE, S. H. (1940). Stability and configuration of the wakes produced by solid bodies moving through fluids. *Phil. Mag.* (7), **29**, 209–57.

HOLSTEIN, H. (1950). Über die äussere und innere Reibungsschicht bei Störungen laminar Strömungen. *Z. angew. Math. Mech.* **30**, 25–49.

HOPF, L. (1914). Der Verlauf kleiner Schwingungen auf einer Strömung reibender Flüssigkeit. *Ann. Phys., Lpz.*, (4), **44**, 1–60.

JEFFREYS, H. (1926). The stability of a layer of fluid heated below. *Phil. Mag.* (7), **2**, 833–44.

JEFFREYS, H. (1928). Some cases of instability in fluid motion. *Proc. Roy. Soc.* A, **118**, 195–208.

JEFFREYS, H. (1930). The instability of a compressible fluid heated below. *Proc. Camb. Phil. Soc.* **26**, 170–2.

JEFFREYS, H. and BLAND, M. E. M. (1951). The instability of a fluid sphere heated within. *Mon. Not. R. Astr. Soc. Geophys. Suppl.* **6**, 148–58.

KÁRMÁN, TH. VON (1924). Über die Stabilität der Laminarströmung und die Theorie der Turbulenz. *Proc. 1st Int. Congr. Appl. Mech.*, Delft, pp. 97–112.

KÁRMÁN, TH. VON (1934). Some aspects of the turbulence problem. *Proc. 4th Int. Congr. Appl. Mech.*, Cambridge, England, pp. 54–91.

KELVIN, LORD (1880). On a disturbing infinity in Lord Rayleigh's solution for waves in a plane vortex stratum. *Mathematical and Physical Papers*, **4**, 186–7. Cambridge University Press.

KELVIN, LORD (1887a). Rectilinear motion of a viscous fluid between parallel planes. *Mathematical and Physical Papers*, **4**, 321–30. Cambridge University Press.

KELVIN, LORD (1887b). Broad river flowing down an inclined plane bed. *Mathematical and Physical Papers*, **4**, 330–7. Cambridge University Press.

KING, L. V. (1916). Theory and experiments relating to the establishment of turbulent flow in pipes and channels. *Phil. Mag.* (6), **31**, 332–8.

KUETHE, A. M. (1950). Some aspects of boundary-layer transition and flow separation on cylinders in yaw. *Proc. Mid-western Conf. on Fluid Dynamics*, pp. 44–55. Ann Arbor, Mich.: J. W. Edwards.

KUO, H. L. (1949). Dynamic instability of two-dimensional non-divergent flow in a barotropic atmosphere. *J. Met.* **6**, 105–22.

KUO, H. L. (1951). Dynamic aspects of the general circulation and the stability of zonal flow. *Tellus*, **3**, 268–84.

KUO, H. L. (1952). Three-dimensional disturbances in a baroclinic zonal current. *J. Met.* **9**, 260–78.

KUO, H. L. (1953a). The stability properties and structure of disturbances in a baroclinic atmosphere. *J. Met.* **10**, 235–43.

KUO, H. L. (1953b). The development of quasi-geostrophic motions in the atmosphere. *Geophys. Res. Pap.* no. 24, pp. 27–52. Cambridge, Mass.: Geophysical Research Directorate.

KUO, H. L. (1953c). On the production of mean zonal currents in the atmosphere by large disturbances. *Tellus*, **5**, 475–93.

LANDAU, L. (1944). Stability of tangential discontinuities in compressible fluid. *C.R. Acad. Sci. U.R.S.S.* **44**, 139–41.

LANGE, A. H., GIESELER, L. P. and LEE, R. E. (1953). Variation of transition Reynolds number with Mach number. *J. Aero. Sci.* **20**, 718–19.

LANGE, A. H. and LEE, R. E. (1954). Note on boundary-layer transition in supersonic flow. *J. Aero. Sci.* **21**, 58.

LANGER, R. E. (1940). On the stability of the laminar flow of a viscous fluid. *Bull. Amer. Math. Soc.* **46**, 257–63.

LAPWOOD, E. R. (1948). Convection of a fluid in a porous medium. *Proc. Camb. Phil. Soc.* **44**, 508–21.

LAURMANN, J. A. (1951). Stability of the compressible laminar boundary layer with an external pressure gradient. *Rep. Coll. Aero. Cranfield*, no. 48.

LEES, L. (1947). The stability of the laminar boundary layer in a compressible fluid. *N.A.C.A. Tech. Rep.*, no. 876, i + 47 pp.; formerly issued as *Tech. Notes*, no. 1360, 144 pp.

LEES, L. (1948). Stability of the laminar boundary layer with injection of cool gas at the wall. *Princeton University Aeronautical Engineering Laboratory Report*, no. 139.

LEES, L. (1949). Stability of the laminar boundary layer in a compressible fluid. *Proc. Symp. Appl. Math.* **1**, 74–80, Amer. Math. Soc.

LEES, L. (1950). Stability of the supersonic laminar boundary layer with a pressure gradient. *Princeton University Aeronautical Engineering Laboratory Report*, no. 167.

LEES, L. (1951). Comments on the 'effect of surface cooling on laminar boundary-layer stability'. *J. Aero. Sci.* **18**, 844.

LEES, L. (1952). Instability of laminar flows and transition to turbulence. *Consolidated Aircraft Corporation Rep. ZA–7–006*, 38 pp. San Diego, California.

LEES, L. and LIN, C. C. (1946). Investigation of the stability of the laminar boundary layer in a compressible fluid. *Tech. Notes Nat. Adv. Comm. Aero., Wash.*, no. 1115, 83 pp.

LESSEN, M. (1950). On stability of free laminar boundary layer between parallel streams. *N.A.C.A. Tech. Rep.*, no. 979, 9 pp. (1950); previously issued as *Tech. Notes*, no. 1929 (1949).

LESSEN, M. (1952a). Note on a sufficient condition for the stability of general plane parallel flows. *Quart. Appl. Math.* **10**, 184–6.

LESSEN, M. (1952b). Some considerations of the stability of laminar parallel flows. *J. Aero. Sci.* **19**, 492.

LESSEN, M. (1953). A remark on the stability of the laminar boundary layer in a compressible fluid. *J. Aero. Sci.* **20**, 500.

LEWIS, D. J. (1950). The instability of liquid surfaces when accelerated in a direction perpendicular to their planes. II. *Proc. Roy. Soc.* A, **202**, 81–96.

LEWIS, J. W. (1928). An experimental study of the motion of a viscous liquid contained between two coaxial cylinders. *Proc. Roy. Soc.* A, **117**, 388–407.

LIEPMANN, H. W. (1943). Investigations on laminar boundary-layer stability and transition on curved boundaries. *N.A.C.A. Rep.* ACR 3 H 30.

LIEPMANN, H. W. (1945). Investigation of boundary layer transition on concave walls. *N.A.C.A. Rep.* ACR 4 J 28.

LIEPMANN, H. W. and FILA, G. H. (1947). Investigations of effects of surface temperature and single roughness elements on boundary-layer transition. *N.A.C.A. Tech. Rep.* no. 890.

LIN, C. C. (1944). On the stability of two-dimensional parallel flows. *Proc. Nat. Acad. Sci., Wash.*, **30**, 316–23.

LIN, C. C. (1945). On the stability of two-dimensional parallel flows. Parts I, II, III. *Quart. Appl. Math.* **3**, 117–42, 218–34, 277–301.

LIN, C. C. (1950). On the stability of zonal winds over a rotating spherical earth. *Proc. Int. Congr. Math.* pp. 632–3.

LIN, C. C. (1952). On the stability of the boundary layer with respect to disturbances of large wave velocity. *J. Aero. Sci.* **19**, 138–9.

LIN, C. C. (1953). On the stability of the laminar mixing region between two parallel streams in a gas. *N.A.C.A. Tech. Notes*, no. 2887.

LIN, C. C. (1954a). Hydrodynamic stability. *Proc. 5th Symp. Appl. Math.* (AMS), pp. 1–18.

LIN, C. C. (1954b). Some physical aspects of the stability of parallel flows. *Proc. Nat. Acad. Sci., Wash.*, **40**, 741–7.

LIN, C. C., WASOW, W. and HOLSTEIN, H. (1951). Letter to the editor of *Z. angew. Math. Mech.* **31**, 159–60.

LINDGREN, E. R. (1954). Some aspects of the change between laminar and turbulent flow of liquids in cylindrical tubes. *Ark. Fys.* **7**, 293–308.

LOCK, R. C. (1954). Hydrodynamic stability of the flow in the laminar boundary layer between parallel streams. *Proc. Camb. Phil. Soc.* **50**, 105–24.

LOFTIN, L. K. and BURROWS, D. L. (1949). Investigations relating to the extension of laminar flow by means of boundary-layer suction through slots. *N.A.C.A. Tech. Notes*, no. 1961.

LORENTZ, H. A. (1907). Über die Entstehung turbulenter Flüssigkeitsbewegungen und über den Einfluss dieser Bewegungen bei der Strömung durch Rohren. *Abh. theor. Phys., Lpz.*, **1**, 43–71.

LOW, A. R. (1929). On the criterion for stability for a layer of viscous fluid heated from below. *Proc. Roy. Soc.* A, **125**, 180–95.

LOW, G. M. (1954). Cooling requirements for stability of laminar boundary layer with small pressure gradient at supersonic speeds. *N.A.C.A. Tech. Notes*, no. 3103.

LYTTLETON, R. A. (1953). *The Stability of Rotating Liquid Masses.* Cambridge University Press.

MACCREADIE, W. T. (1931). On the stability of the motion of a viscous fluid. *Proc. Nat. Acad. Sci., Wash.*, **17**, 381–8.

MEKSYN, D. (1946a). Fluid motion between parallel planes. Dynamic stability. *Proc. Roy. Soc.* A, **186**, 391–409.

MEKSYN, D. (1946b). Stability of viscous flow between rotating cylinders. I, II, III. *Proc. Roy. Soc.* A, **187**, 115–28, 480–91, 492–504.

MEKSYN, D. (1948). Note on stability of laminar viscous flow between parallel planes. *Proc. Roy. Soc.* A, **195**, 174–9.

MEKSYN, D. (1950). Stability of viscous flow over concave cylindrical surfaces. *Proc. Roy. Soc.* A, **203**, 253–65.

MEKSYN, D. and STUART, J. T. (1951). Stability of viscous motion between parallel planes for finite disturbances. *Proc. Roy. Soc.* A, **208**, 517–26.

MICHAEL, D. H. (1953). Stability of plane parallel flows of electrically conducting fluids. *Proc. Camb. Phil. Soc.* **49**, 166–8.

MISES, R. VON (1912a). Kleine Schwingungen und Turbulenz. *Jber. dtsch. MatVer.* **21**, 241–8.

MISES, R. VON (1912b). *Beitrag zum Oszillationsproblem.* Festschrift Heinrich Weber, pp. 252–82. Leipzig und Berlin: Teubner.

MORAWETZ, C. S. (1952). The eigenvalues of some stability problems involving viscosity. *J. Rat. Mech. Anal.* **1**, 579–603.

MORAWETZ, C. S. (1954). Asymptotic solutions of the stability equations of a compressible fluid. *J. Math. Phys.* **33**, 1–26.

NEAMTAN, S. M. (1946). The motion of harmonic waves in the atmosphere. *J. Met.* **3**, 53–6.

NOETHER, F. (1913). On the generation of a turbulent fluid motion. *S.B. bayer Akad. Wiss.* pp. 309–29.

NOETHER, F. (1914). On the theory of turbulence. *Jber. dtsch. MatVer.* **23**, 138–44.

NOETHER, F. (1921). Das Turbulenzproblem. *Z. angew. Math. Mech.* **1**, 125–38, 218–19.

NOETHER, F. (1926). Zur asymptotischen Behandlung der stationären Lösungen im Turbulenzproblem. *Z. angew. Math. Mech.* **6**, 232–43, 339–40, 428, 497–8.

ORR, W. McF. (1906–1907). The stability or instability of the steady motions of a liquid. *Proc. R. Irish Acad.* A, **27**, 9–27, 69–138.

PAI, S. I. (1950). On the stability for a certain degenerate type of disturbance of viscous flow between parallel walls. *J. Aero. Sci.* **17**, 525.

PAI, S. I. (1951). On the stability of two-dimensional laminar jet flow of gas. *J. Aero. Sci.* **18**, 731–42.

PAI, S. I. (1954a). On the stability of a vortex sheet in an inviscid compressible fluid. *J. Aero. Sci.* **21**, 325–8.

PAI, S. I. (1954b). On a generalization of Synge's criterion for sufficient stability of plane parallel flows. *Quart. Appl. Math.* **12**, 203–6.

PARKER, E. N. (1953). Extension of Heisenberg's model of turbulence to critical Reynolds numbers. *Phys. Rev.* **90**, 221–2.

PEKERIS, C. L. (1936). On the stability problem in hydrodynamics. *Proc. Camb. Phil. Soc.* **32**, 55–66.

PEKERIS, C. L. (1938). On the stability problem in hydrodynamics. II. *J. Aero. Sci.* **5**, 237–40.

PEKERIS, C. L. (1948a). Stability of the laminar flow through a straight pipe of circular cross-section to infinitesimal disturbances which are symmetrical about the axis of the pipe. *Proc. Nat. Acad. Sci., Wash.*, **34**, 285–95.

PEKERIS, C. L. (1948b). Stability of the laminar parabolic flow of a viscous fluid between parallel fixed walls. *Phys. Rev.* (2), **74**, 191–9.

PELLEW, A. and SOUTHWELL, R. V. (1940). On maintained convective motion in a fluid heated from below. *Proc. Roy. Soc.* A, **176**, 312–43.

PLATZMANN, G. W. (1952). The increase or decrease of mean-flow energy in large-scale horizontal flow in the atmosphere. *J. Met.* 9, 347–58.

PRANDTL, L. (1921–1926). Bemerkungen über die Entstehung der Turbulenz. *Z. angew. Math. Mech.* 1, 431–6 (1921); also *Phys. Z.* 23, 19–23 (1922). See also the discussion after Solberg's paper (1924) and that with F. Noether, *Z. angew. Math. Mech.* 6, 339, 428 (1926).

PRANDTL, L. (1929). Einfluss stabilisierender Kräfte auf die Turbulenz. *Vorträge aus dem Gebiete der Aerodynamik und verwandter Gebiete, Aachen,* 1930, pp. 1–17. Berlin: Julius Springer.

PRANDTL, L. (1935). Article in *Aerodynamic Theory,* edited by W. F. Durand, 3, 178–90. Berlin: Julius Springer.

PRETSCH, J. (1941a). Über die Stabilität einer Laminarströmung um ein Kugel. *Luftfahrtforsch.* 18, 341–4.

PRETSCH, J. (1941b). Die Stabilität einer ebenen Laminarströmung bei Druckgefälle und Druckansteig. *Jb. dtsch. Luftfahrtf. Zbl. Wiss. Ber.-Wes.* 1, 158–175.

PRETSCH, J. (1941c). Über die Stabilität einer Laminarströmung in einem geraden Rohr mit Kreisförmigen Querschnitt. *Z. angew. Math. Mech.* 21, 204–17.

PRETSCH, J. (1942a). Umschlagbeginn und Absaugung. *Jb. dtsch. Luftfahrtf. Zbl. Wiss. Ber.-Wes.* 1, 1–7.

PRETSCH, J. (1942b). Die Anfachung instabler Störungen in einer laminaren Reibungsschicht. *Jb. dtsch. Luftfahrtf.* pp. 154–71.

QUENEY, P. (1950). Adiabatic perturbation equations for a zonal atmospheric current. *Tellus,* 2, 35–51.

RAYLEIGH, LORD (1878). On the instability of jets. *Scientific Papers,* 1, 361–71. Cambridge University Press.

RAYLEIGH, LORD (1880). On the stability, or instability, of certain fluid motions. *Scientific Papers,* 1, 474–87. Cambridge University Press.

RAYLEIGH, LORD (1887). On the stability, or instability, of certain fluid motions. II. *Scientific Papers,* 3, 2–23. Cambridge University Press.

RAYLEIGH, LORD (1892a). On the question of the stability of the flow of fluids. *Scientific Papers,* 3, 575–84. Cambridge University Press.

RAYLEIGH, LORD (1892b). On the instability of a cylinder of viscous liquid under capillary force. *Scientific Papers,* 3, 585–93. Cambridge University Press.

RAYLEIGH, LORD (1892c). On the instability of cylindrical fluid surfaces. *Scientific Papers,* 3, 594–6. Cambridge University Press.

RAYLEIGH, LORD (1895). On the stability or instability of certain fluid motions. III. *Scientific Papers,* 4, 203–9. Cambridge University Press.

RAYLEIGH, LORD (1913). On the stability of the laminar motion of an inviscid fluid. *Scientific Papers,* 6, 197–204. Cambridge University Press.

RAYLEIGH, LORD (1914). Further remarks on the stability of viscous fluid motion. *Scientific Papers,* 6, 266–75. Cambridge University Press.

RAYLEIGH, LORD (1915). On the stability of the simple shearing motion of a viscous incompressible fluid. *Scientific Papers*, **6**, 341–9. Cambridge University Press.

RAYLEIGH, LORD (1916a). On convection currents in a horizontal layer of fluid when the higher temperature is on the under side. *Scientific Papers*, **6**, 432–46. Cambridge University Press.

RAYLEIGH, LORD (1916b). On the dynamics of revolving fluids. *Scientific Papers*, **6**, 447–53. Cambridge University Press.

REYNOLDS, O. (1895). On the dynamical theory of incompressible viscous fluids and the determination of the criterion. *Scientific Papers*, **2**, 535–77. Cambridge University Press.

ROSENBROOK, G. (1937). Instabilität der Gleitschicht im schwach divergenten Kanal. *Z. angew. Math. Mech.* **17**, 8–24.

ROSSBY, C. G. (1949). On a mechanism for the release of potential energy in the atmosphere. *J. Met.* **6**, 163–80.

ROUSE, H. (1945). A general stability index for flow near plane boundaries. *J. Aero. Sci.* **12**, 429–31. See also Liepmann's letter to the editor, *J. Aero. Sci.* **13**, 94.

SAVIC, P. (1941). On acoustically effective vortex motion in gaseous jets. *Phil. Mag.* (7), **32**, 245–52.

SAVIC, P. and MURPHY, J. W. (1943). The symmetrical vortex street in sound-sensitive plane jets. *Phil. Mag.* (7), **34**, 139–44.

SCHERRER, R., WEINBROW, W. R. and GOWEN, F. E. (1949). Heat transfer and boundary-layer transition on a heated 20° cone at a Mach number of 1·53. *N.A.C.A.* RM A8L28.

SCHILLER, L. (1925). Das Turbulenzproblem und verwandte Fragen. *Phys. Z.* **26**, 566–95, 632.

SCHLICHTING, H. (1932a). Über die Stabilität der Couetteströmung. *Ann. Phys., Lpz.*, **14**, 905–36.

SCHLICHTING, H. (1932b). Über die Enstehung der Turbulenz in einem rotierenden Zylinder. *Nachr. Ges. Wiss. Göttingen*, Math.-phys. Klasse, pp. 160–98.

SCHLICHTING, H. (1933a). Zur Entstehung der Turbulenz bei der Plattenströmung. *Nachr. Ges. Wiss. Göttingen*, Math.-phys. Klasse, pp. 181–208.

SCHLICHTING, H. (1933b). Berechnung der Anfachung kleiner Störungen bei der Plattenströmung. *Z. angew. Math. Mech.* **13**, 171–4.

SCHLICHTING, H. (1934). Neuere Untersuchungen über die Turbulenzentstehung. *Naturwissenschaften*, **22**, 376–81.

SCHLICHTING, H. (1935a). Amplitudenverteilung und Energiebilanz der kleinen Störungen bei der Plattengrenzschicht. *Nachr. Ges. Wiss. Göttingen*, Math.-phys. Klasse, **1**, 47–78.

SCHLICHTING, H. (1935b). Turbulenz bei Wärmeschichtung. *Z. angew. Math. Mech.* **15**, 313.

SCHLICHTING, H. and ULRICH, A. (1940). Zur Berechung des Umschlages laminar-turbulent. *Ber. Lilienthal-Ges.* **10**, 75.

SCHLICHTING, H. and ULRICH, A. (1942). Über die Berechnung der Umschlagsstelle laminar-turbulent. *J. dtsch. Luftfahrtf.* **1**, 8–35.

SCHMIDT, R. J. and MILVERTON, S. W. (1935). On the instability of a fluid when heated from below. *Proc. Roy. Soc.* A, **152**, 586–94.

SCHUBAUER, G. B. and SKRAMSTAD, H. K. (1943). Laminar boundary layer oscillations and transition on a flat plate. *N.A.C.A. Tech. Rep.* no. 909 (1948). Originally issued as *N.A.C.A. A.C.R.* (April, 1943).

SCHUBAUER, G. B. and SKRAMSTAD, H. K. (1947). Laminar boundary-layer oscillations and transition on a flat plate. *J. Aero. Sci.* **14**, 69–78; *J. Res. Nat. Bur. Stand.* **38**, 251–92.

SEXL, T. (1927a). Zur Stabilitätsfrage der Poiseuilleschen and Couetteschen Strömung. *Ann. Phys., Lpz.*, **83**, 835–48.

SEXL, T. (1927b). Über dreidimensionale Störungen der Poiseuilleschen Strömung. *Ann. Phys., Lpz.*, (4), **84**, 807–22.

SHARPE, F. R. (1905). On the stability of the motion of a viscous liquid. *Trans. Amer. Math. Soc.* **6**, 496–503.

SHEN, S. F. (1954). Calculated amplified oscillations in plane Poiseuille and Blasius flows. *J. Aero. Sci.* **21**, 62–4.

SOLBERG, H. (1924). Zum Turbulenzproblem. *Proc. 1st Int. Congr. Appl. Mech.*, Delft, pp. 387–94.

SOLBERG, H. (1930). Das Zyklonenproblem. *Proc. 3rd Int. Congr. Appl. Mech.* **1**, 121–31.

SOMMERFELD, A. (1908). Ein Beitrag zur hydrodynamischen Erklärung der turbulenten Flüssigkeitsbewegung. *Proc. 4th Int. Congr. Math.* Rome, pp. 116–24.

SOUTHWELL, R. V. (1924). Note on the stability of laminar shearing motion in a viscous incompressible fluid. *Phil. Mag.* **48**, 540–53.

SOUTHWELL, R. V. and CHITTY, L. (1930). On the problem of hydrodynamic stability. I. Uniform shearing motion in a viscous liquid. *Phil. Trans.* A, **229**, 205–83; *Rep. Memor. Aero. Res. Comm., Lond.*, no. 1200.

SQUIRE, H. B. (1933). On the stability of the three-dimensional disturbances of viscous flow between parallel walls. *Proc. Roy. Soc.* A, **142**, 621–8.

STARR, V. P. (1951). A note on the eddy transport of angular momentum. *Quart. J. R. Met. Soc.* **77**, 44–50.

STERNBERG, J. (1952). A free-flight investigation of the possibility of high Reynolds number supersonic laminar boundary layers. *J. Aero. Sci.* **19**, 721–33.

STUART, J. T. (1954). On the stability of viscous flow between parallel planes in the presence of a co-planar magnetic field. *Proc. Roy. Soc.* A, **221**, 189–206.

SUTTON, O. G. (1950). On the stability of a fluid heated from below. *Proc. Roy. Soc.* A, **204**, 297–309.

SYNGE, J. L. (1933). The stability of heterogeneous liquids. *Trans. Roy. Soc. Can.* **27**, 1–18.

SYNGE, J. L. (1936). The stability of quadratic velocity distribution for an inviscid liquid flowing between parallel planes. *J. Math. Phys.* **15**, 205–10.

SYNGE, J. L. (1938a). On the stability of a viscous liquid between two rotating coaxial cylinders. *Proc. Roy. Soc.* A, **167**, 250–6.

SYNGE, J. L. (1938b). *Hydrodynamic Stability.* Semi-centennial publications of the Amer. Math. Soc. **2** (Addresses), 227–69.

SYNGE, J. L. (1938c). The stability of plane Poiseuille motion. *Proc. 5th Int. Congr. Appl. Math.*, Cambridge, U.S.A., pp. 326–32.

TAMAKI, K. and HARRISON, W. J. (1920). On the stability of the steady motion of viscous liquid contained between rotating coaxial cylinders. *Trans. Camb. Phil. Soc.* **22**, 425–48.

TATSUMI, T. (1952a). Stability of the laminar inlet-flow prior to the formation of Poiseuille Regime. I, II. *J. Phys. Soc. Japan*, **7**, 489–95, 495–502.

TATSUMI, T. (1952b). Note on discrepancies between two theories on the stability of plane Poiseuille flow. *J. Phys. Soc. Japan*, **7**, 619–24.

TAYLOR, G. I. (1923). Stability of a viscous liquid contained between two rotating cylinders. *Phil. Trans.* A, **223**, 289–343.

TAYLOR, G. I. (1924). Experiments with rotating fluids. *Proc. 1st Int Congr. Appl. Mech.* pp. 89–96.

TAYLOR, G. I. (1931). Effect of variation in density on the stability of superposed streams of fluid. *Proc. Roy. Soc.* A, **132**, 499–523.

TAYLOR, G. I. (1936a). Statistical theory of turbulence. V. Effect of turbulence on boundary layer. *Proc. Roy. Soc.* A, **156**, 307–17.

TAYLOR, G. I. (1936b). Oscillations of the atmosphere. *Proc. Roy. Soc.* A, **156**, 318–26.

TAYLOR, G. I. (1938). Some recent developments in the study of turbulence. *Proc. 5th Int. Congr. Appl. Mech.*, Cambridge, U.S.A., pp. 294–310.

TAYLOR, G. I. (1950). The instability of liquid surfaces when accelerated in a direction perpendicular to their planes. I. *Proc. Roy. Soc.* A, **201**, 192–4.

TETERVIN, N. (1953). A study of the stability of the incompressible laminar boundary layer on infinite wedges. *N.A.C.A. Tech. Notes*, no. 2976.

TETERVIN, N. and LEVINE, D. A. (1952). A study of the stability of the laminar boundary layer as affected by changes in the boundary-layer thickness in regions of pressure gradient and flow through the surface. *N.A.C.A. Tech. Notes*, no. 2752.

THOMAS, L. H. (1953). The stability of plane Poiseuille flow. *Phys. Rev.* (2), **91**, 780–3.

THOMAS, T. Y. (1942). Qualitative analysis of the flow of fluids in pipes. *Amer. J. Math.* **64**, 754–67.

THOMAS, T. Y. (1943). On the uniform convergence of the solutions of the Navier-Stokes equations. *Proc. Nat. Acad. Sci., Wash.*, **29**, 243–6.

THOMAS, T. Y. (1944). On the stability of viscous fluids. *Univ. Calif. Publ. Math.* **2**, 13–43.

THOMPSON, P. D. (1953). On the theory of large-scale disturbances in a two-dimensional baroclinic equivalent of the atmosphere. *Quart. J. R. Met. Soc.* **79**, 51–69.

THOMPSON, W. B. (1949). Thermal convection in a magnetic field. *Proc. 2nd Canadian Math. Congr.*, Vancouver, pp. 196–205.

THOMPSON, W. B. (1951). Thermal convection in a magnetic field. *Phil. Mag.* (7) **42**, 1417–32.

TIETJENS, O. (1925). Beiträge zur Entstehung der Turbulenz. *Z. angew. Math. Mech.* **5**, 200–17.

TOLLMIEN, W. (1929). Über die Entstehung der Turbulenz. *Nachr. Ges. Wiss. Göttingen*, Math.-phys. Klasse, pp. 21–44; see also *Vorträge aus dem Gebiete der Aerodynamik und verwandte Gebiete*, Aachen (ed. Gilles, Hopf, von Kármán), pp. 18–21.

TOLLMIEN, W. (1930). Beitrag zur Theorie der Turbulenz. *Proc. 3rd Int. Congr. Appl. Mech.*, Stockholm, **1**, 105–8.

TOLLMIEN, W. (1935a). Über die Korrelation der Geschwindigkeitskomponenten in periodisch schwankenden Wirbelverteilungen. *Z. angew. Math. Mech.* **15**, 96–100.

TOLLMIEN, W. (1935b). Ein allgemeines Kriterium der Instabilität laminarer Geschwindigkeitsverteilungen. *Nachr. Ges. Wiss. Göttingen*, Math.-phys. Klasse, **50**, 79–114.

TOLLMIEN, W. (1947). Asymptoticsche Integration der Störungsdifferentialgleichung ebener laminarer Strömungen bei hohen Reynoldsschen Zahlen. *Z. angew. Math. Mech.* **25/27**, 33–50, 70–83.

TOLLMIEN, W. (1948). Laminare Grenzschichten, Hydro- and Aerodynamics. *F.I.A.T. Rev. German Sci.* 1939–46. Wiesbaden.

TOLLMIEN, W. (1953a). Laminare Grenzschichten. *Naturforschung und Medizin in Deutschland*, 1939–47, **11**. Hydro- und Aerodynamik, pp. 21–53. Verlag Chemie Weinheim.

TOLLMIEN, W. (1953b). Fortschritte der Turbulenzforschung. *Z. angew. Math. Mech.* **33**, 200–11.

TRILLING, L. (1950). The incompressible boundary layer with pressure gradient and suction. *J. Aero. Sci.* **17**, 335–42.

ULRICH, A. (1944). Theoretische Untersuchungen über die Widerstandsersparnis durch Laminarhaltung durch Absaugung. *Schr. dtsch. Akad. Luftfahrtf.* **8**B, 53 (translated as *N.A.C.A. Tech. Memo.*, no. 1121, 1947).

VAN DRIEST, E. R. (1951). Cooling required to stabilize the laminar boundary layer on a flat plate. *J. Aero. Sci.* **18**, 698–9.

VAN DRIEST, E. R. (1952). Calculation of the stability of the laminar boundary layer in a compressible fluid on a flat plate with heat transfer. *J. Aero. Sci.* **19**, 801–12.

WASOW, W. (1948). The complex asymptotic theory of a fourth order differential equation of hydrodynamics. *Ann. Math.* (2), **49**, 852–71.

WASOW, W. (1950). A study of the solution of the differential equation $y^{\mathrm{IV}} + \lambda^2(xy'' + y) = 0$ for large values of λ. *Ann. Math.* **52**, 350–61.

WASOW, W. (1953a). One small disturbance of plane Couette flow. *J. Res. Nat. Bur. Stand.* **51**, 195–202.

WASOW, W. (1953b). Asymptotic solution of the differential equation of hydrodynamic stability in a domain containing a transition point. *Ann. Math.* **58**, 222–52.

WEIL, H. (1951). Effects of pressure gradient on stability and skin friction in laminar boundary layers in compressible fluids. *J. Aero. Sci.* **18**, 311–18.

WUEST, W. (1953). Nahrungsweise Berechnung und Stabilitätsverhalten von laminar Grenzschichten mit Absaugung durch Einzelschlitze. *Ingen. Arch.* **21**, 90–103.